REACH FOR THE STARS!

Let Your Imagination Soar

Happy writing!

Young Author's Fiction Workbook

Susan K. Marlow

Media Angels®, Inc.
Fort Myers, Florida

Reach for the Stars: Young Author's Fiction Workbook

© 2009 Susan K. Marlow

Published by Media Angels®, Inc.
Fort Myers, Florida 33912
www.MediaAngels.com/ReachfortheStars

ISBN: 978-1-931941-19-8

Cover layout by Jessica Hammer

Interior pages layout by Susan K. Marlow

Clipart used as per license agreement
Art Explosion Image Library Nova Development Corporation

Contents

Note to Parents:

Get ready to blast off on a journey of imagination! *Reach for the Stars* includes all the writing tools your child needs to create a fiction story from first idea to finished manuscript. The only thing this book does *not* include is the "fuel" to put your young author's writing adventure into orbit—his or her own unique storehouse of ideas. This should not be a problem, however. Most children overflow with wonder, imagination, and crazy ideas. It's only we adults who somehow lose that spark as we grow older. *Reach for the Stars* gives children a place to keep their ideas, organize them, and express those ideas in readable stories.

Reach for the Stars can be used in more than one way:

1) You can work together and guide your child through the writing activities by using the "Especially for Teachers and Parents" lesson ideas at the back of the book (pp. 139-140).

2) Older students can use this book on their own. The instructions are intended to be kid-friendly and easy to follow.

3) *Reach for the Stars* also works well in classrooms and co-ops.

Many begin stories. Few finish the task. Even if your child does not come away with a completed story—beginning to end—he will still have acquired the tools to write in the future. The skills presented in *Reach for the Stars* can be used for both fiction and non-fiction.

 # Ideas, Ideas, Ideas

The seed of a story is the idea. Some writers have a million ideas chasing around in their heads. Others want to create a story but can't think of a thing to write. If you're "stuck on the launching pad," here are some suggestions to help you lift off:

♦ Do you have a favorite book series? A character you love to read about? Use that character to write a new adventure, based on the series. The same thing applies to favorite movies. For example: Write a new episode using your favorite characters from *The Chronicles of Narnia*. True, you will never see your story published (copyright laws), but it will jumpstart your imagination and help get you writing.

♦ Is there a place you've always dreamed of going? Something you've always wanted to do? Put yourself in the story and write down everything that could happen to you there.

♦ Ask the "What If?" question. Later in the book we will create characters. You plop your character down in a setting (where and when) and then ask a writer's favorite question: "What if . . .?" What if Joe were walking down the road and he fell into a hole that led to a different dimension? What if Sarah woke up and discovered it was raining quarters? Ask this question whenever you get stuck writing your story.

♦ *Brainstorm.* Another favorite trick of writers. Brainstorming is writing down any ideas that pop into your head, no matter how silly. Some writers draw fancy diagrams with circles or story "webs." I just like to jot down ideas on lined paper and organize them later. The silly ideas I cross out, but sometimes a silly idea can lead to an interesting plot twist.

- Find pictures of what your characters might look like and where they live (the setting). Cut out pictures of their favorite things, like a fancy car. Find pictures of unusual objects your character might have, like the spaceship you imagine they command.

- If you want to write a story that takes place in the past, you may want to find out some *real* history facts through research. Print out timelines and other information about the time period.

Now that you've thought of a few ideas, where do you keep them? Your head is *not* the best place to keep your story ideas. Writing them down is the best way. The next few pages are empty. They are brainstorming pages. Any time during the course of this book, you can flip to these pages and fill them up with ideas about your characters, things that happen to your characters, or new story ideas. Keep this book nearby. If an idea pops into your head, write it down!

This space is for a pocket to keep photos or drawings of your characters and settings. Older students may want to keep research tidbits they come across.

To make the folder:

- Cut out a piece of light-weight cardstock (the weight of a file folder works best).

- Measure it to fit the bottom half of this page and trim.

- Use clear packing tape to secure the sides and the bottom of the pocket to this page. (You will cover this text)

- Decorate and/or write "IDEAS" on the outside of the pocket.

Brainstorming Pages

_____

_____

_____

_____

_____

_____

_____

_____

_____

_____

_____

_____

_____

_____

_____

_____

_____

_____

_____

_____

Brainstorming

_____

_____

_____

_____

_____

_____

_____

_____

_____

_____

_____

_____

_____

_____

_____

_____

_____

_____

_____

_____

_____

_____

_____

_____

_____

_____

Brainstorming

_____

_____

_____

_____

_____

_____

_____

_____

_____

_____

_____

_____

_____

_____

_____

_____

_____

_____

_____

_____

_____

_____

Brainstorming

_____

_____

_____

_____

_____

_____

_____

_____

_____

_____

_____

_____

_____

_____

_____

_____

_____

_____

_____

_____

_____

_____

_____

Who's It For?

Authors write books for different reasons and for different people (their audiences). Some authors write only for themselves. It's important to learn to tell the difference. Why? So you can decide for whom you want to write and for what reasons. Can you guess for whom these different types of books are written? Choose words from the boxes below to fill in the blanks:

<u>**Author's Audience**</u>

-others

-himself / herself

<u>**Author's Purpose**</u>

-to entertain

-to inform (teach)

-to reflect and record thoughts

Journals- (Example: *The Diary of Anne Frank*)

The author's purpose is to _____

The author's audience is _____

Expository Writing- (Example: *All About Snakes and Reptiles*)

The author's purpose is to _____

The author's audience is _____

Narrative Stories- (Example: The Chronicles of Narnia)

The author's purpose is to _____

The author's audience is _____

Narrative stories are split into two kinds of stories

Personal Experiences

Little Britches

Caddie Woodlawn

Biographies

Character-Problem-Solution

The Forgotten Door

The Black Stallion

Mysteries

It's Your Turn

Go on a book hunt and see if you can identify Journals, Expository books, Narrative "Personal Experience," and Narrative "Character-Problem-Solution" books. When you read a book during the next few weeks, add it to the list below. Try to identify the "genre" (john-ra) [kind].

"X" the correct box. (Some books can fall into two categories.)

<u>Remember:</u> *Journals* are like diaries. They are usually written for an audience of one—the author.

Expository books are like textbooks. The author wants to teach you something.

Narrative books can be *personal experiences*—a day at the zoo or a biography of someone's life. *Narrative* books can also be about a *character who needs to solve a problem.* Most fiction stories fall into the character-problem-solution genre.

Title of Book	Journal	Expository	Narrative: Personal Experience	Narrative: Character Problem Solution
War of the Worlds				X
All About Snakes and Reptiles		X		
All-of-a-Kind-Family			X	

The Five Elements of a [Good] Fiction Story

The stories you will learn to write using this book are the Narrative: CHARACTER—PROBLEM—SOLUTION genre [kind]. Of course, you can write a personal experience-type story as well, but it's good to know how most fiction books are created.

Writing a story is like putting together a puzzle. When you finish your puzzle and discover a piece or two missing, how do you feel about the puzzle?

_____

_____

_____

_____

I feel unhappy . . . and cheated out of a satisfying end to all my hard work.

It's the same way with a story. There are five elements (pieces) of a good fiction story. When you put them together, your story shines. Leave one piece out, and it falls flat. <u>Memorize these five elements!</u>

~CHARACTER~

~SETTING~

~PROBLEM~

~PLOT~

~SOLUTION~

The 5 Elements

An appealing CHARACTER:

This should be someone with whom the reader can relate. You want the reader to care about your main character and what happens to him or her.

An interesting SETTING:

Put your character in an unusual setting, like the dark side of the moon or in an old castle. An example of a unique setting for a story is the book *Holes*.

An intriguing PROBLEM:

Once you put your character in a setting, give him a problem to solve. Not like a math problem, but a quest, an adventure, or a chance to grow and change as a character. Then make the problem worse!

An exciting PLOT:

"Plot" is another word for the events that happen in the story while the character is trying to solve his problem, however big or small it might be. A lot of "ups" and "downs" happen along the way. The plot is where you answer the "What If?" questions.

A satisfying SOLUTION:

When your character has solved his problem (or at least come to grips with it), then end your story with a solution that leaves the reader saying, "Ah, that was a good story."

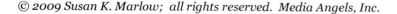

For Example

Here are the 5 elements for the book, *The Lion, the Witch, and the Wardrobe.* Notice I only gave a couple of "plot" events. (You do this on the next page)

Title of book: _The Lion, the Witch, and the Wardrobe_

Main character: _Peter, Susan, Edmund, and Lucy_

Other characters: _Aslan, the White Witch, Mr. Tumnus, Mr. and Mrs. Beaver_

Setting: Time: _World War II_   Place: _England and Narnia_

Problem the character faces: _Peter and his siblings must free the land of Narnia, which lies under the spell of the White Witch_

The plot (2 or 3 events that happen as the character seeks to solve his problem): _Lucy wanders into a wardrobe and discovers Narnia; Edmund meets the White Witch and eats Turkish Delight; Mr. Tumnus is turned into a statue; Aslan offers his life in exchange for Edumund's freedom; Aslan comes back to life; Peter and his siblings meet the Beavers;_

Solution: _Peter and his siblings, with the help of Aslan, fight a great battle and defeat the White Witch. The four children become kings and queens of Narnia._

It's Your Turn

Think of a favorite book (or movie). Does the story include each of the 5 elements?

Title of book: _____

Main character: _____

Other characters: _____

_____

Setting: Time: _____ Place: _____

Problem the character faces: _____

_____

_____

The plot (2 or 3 events that happen as the character seeks to solve

his problem): _____

_____

_____

_____

_____

_____

Solution: _____

_____

_____

What about YOUR Story?

Now think of a story YOU would like to write. Does your story include each of the 5 elements? If you're not ready, you can come back to this section later. **Note:** You can start a story anytime on the computer or on pages at the back of this book!

Title of book: _____

Main character: _____

Other characters: _____

_____

Setting: Time: _____ Place: _____

Problem the character faces: _____

_____

_____

The plot (2 or 3 events that happen as the character seeks to solve

his problem): _____

_____

_____

_____

_____

_____

Solution: _____

_____

_____

_____

What about YOUR Story?

Here is a page for another story you may wish to create, or to practice the 5 elements with another favorite book or movie.

Title of book: _____

Main character: _____

Other characters: _____

_____

Setting: Time: _____ Place: _____

Problem the character faces: _____

_____

_____

_____

The plot (2 or 3 events that happen as the character seeks to solve

his problem): _____

_____

_____

_____

_____

_____

Solution: _____

_____

_____

For Younger Students

Use this puzzle to help you remember the 5 elements of a story.

Instructions:

- Cut around the outside edge of the puzzle.
- Use a glue stick and attach the puzzle to a piece of heavy card stock (an old file folder works well). Allow to dry completely.
- Carefully cut out the puzzle pieces.
- Store the puzzle pieces in your Idea Folder on page 8.

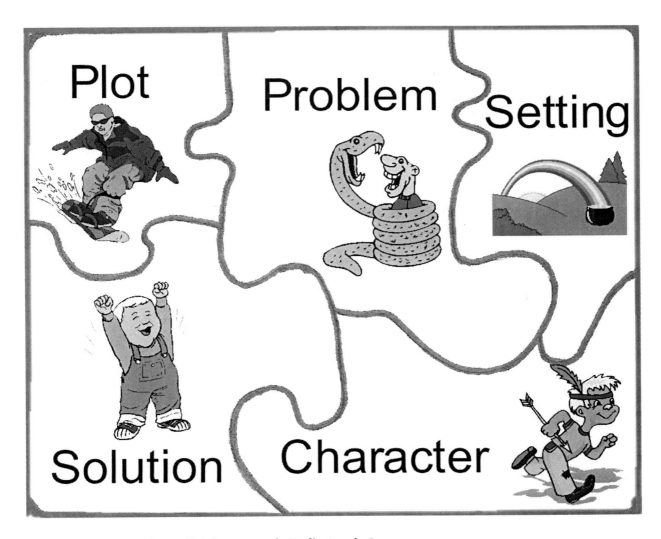

Creating Characters

The Good, the Bad, + the Ugly,

Do your best to create them well,

'Cause if you get slack, you'll find that you lack

A story that *EVER* will sell!

Writer's Hint

Every good fiction story begins with a CHARACTER. Without a strong main character, you have no story.

To create a believable "lead" character for your story:

   1) Choose someone you like and/or admire, and

   2) Someone who has the most to gain or lose in the story.

   3) He/she can be a person, an animal, or even a gold nugget.

Before you create a character of your own, think about why you like certain characters from a favorite book, a movie, or a TV show. Are they funny? Strong? Honest? What about the bad guys? Why do certain book characters make you dislike them?

Write the name of a character you like: _____

Write the name of a character you don't like or are afraid of (the bad guy): _____

On the next pages, write a few sentences explaining what you like about the character and why. Then write a few sentences about why you don't like the "bad guy." Do this "warm-up" as many times as you need with other favorite characters from the books you read. Why? As you discover how authors and movie-makers create their characters, it will help you understand what makes a character appealing so you can create your own.

It's Your Turn

<u>Example</u>: My favorite character is Peter (*The Lion, the Witch, and the Wardrobe*). He is a determined young man with lots of spirit and courage. He looks after his younger sisters, especially Lucy, and he is kind. He also realizes that he can't win battles on his own, but must rely on Aslan to help him. Peter is a real hero!

Name of favorite character: _____

_____

_____

_____

_____

_____

Example: The character I like least is the White Witch from *The Lion, the Witch, and the Wardrobe.* She is evil and cunning. Power is what she is after, and she'll do anything to have control over everyone in Narnia. When she raises her icy wand to turn someone into stone, I shiver. I'm glad Aslan defeated her!

Name of least favorite character: _____

_____

_____

_____

_____

_____

Favorite Characters

"I would make a wonderful lead character for your story—if only someone would get these teeth off my tail!"

Character's name: _____

_____

_____

_____

_____

_____

_____

_____

Character's name: _____

_____

_____

_____

_____

_____

_____

_____

Least-Favorite Characters

Character's name: _____

_____

_____

_____

_____

_____

_____

_____

_____

Character's name: _____

_____

_____

_____

_____

_____

_____

_____

_____

Create Your Characters

Creating a fiction character can be the most interesting thing you do when writing your story. It's also lots of fun. You can make your character look and act exactly as you want. Use your imagination. The sky's the limit!

****
Writer's Hint

A baby name book is a great place to find just the right names for your characters. You can also learn what the names mean.
****

Here's a place where you can brainstorm names of characters. Don't just think of names for your main character and his friends. Come up with names for the antagonists (bad guys), too. Find out what the names mean. Sometimes that will help you create a personality. For example, the name "Dolores" is Spanish for "sorrow." Does this meaning put a picture in your mind of what Dolores might be like? Of course, you can also make names up and invent your own meanings. Have fun!

_____

_____

_____

_____

_____

_____

_____

Character Traits

Once you decide on a name for your character, you can begin to imagine what she or he (or "it") looks like. What a character is like on the outside is called his "Physical Traits." You may want to find a picture of your new character. (Keep your pictures in the pocket on page 8).

Your character also needs a personality—something that makes him unique, or one of a kind. These are called "Personality Traits." The main character usually has a number of good things going for him—he's truthful, adventurous, or loyal. The "bad guy" (antagonist) usually is full of negative traits—cruel, sneaky, or selfish.

Study the chart on the next page for ideas you can use to create your characters' physical and personality traits. It is not a complete listing, but it will help you get started.

Writer's Hint

Believable characters—just like people—have both "good" traits and "bad" traits. The best hero still has a weak trait he needs to work on. The worst enemy has a spark of good. Make sure your characters have both. This makes them real to readers.

Character Charts

You will find Character Charts on the next few pages. Use them to write notes about your characters. What do they look like? How do they act? What are their likes and dislikes? Jotting down notes about your characters makes them become real to you. Once you "know" your characters, the things they do and the choices they make will be exactly what you would expect from them. The list below will give you ideas.

PHYSICAL TRAITS		PERSONALITY TRAITS	
Long/short hair	Eyes & face:	Positive Traits:	Negative Traits:
Color: Black, brown, red, blond, white Style: curly, frizzy, Mohawk, shaved, braided, tangled, combed, wild, bald, long, short, pigtails, thick, glossy, thin, limp Skin: rough, smooth, any color, freckled sunburns easily, tans, transparent Build: tall, athletic, short, clumsy, fat, thin, strong, agile, slow-mover Arms/Legs: Long fingers, short legs, missing fingers, limps, missing toes	Color: Blue, brown, hazel, gray, golden, black, pale Shape: round, narrow, close-set, wide apart, squinty, bulging, deep-set Face: narrow, pinched, hollow cheeks; chubby, full, round cheeks; ears that stick out, bushy eyebrows, long lashes; crooked or missing teeth; straight, white teeth, smiley, frowns, chews on lip; moustache, beard, pimples, dirty face	Friendly, outgoing, confident, cheerful, adventurous, kind, courageous, trusting, high-spirited, bold, determined, content, truthful, obedient, generous, lively, strong-willed, loyal, dependable, patient, diligent, peaceful, responsible, flexible, sensitive, open-minded, hospitable, humble, creative, forgiving, responsible, has self-control	Quick- tempered, impulsive, cruel, gives up quickly, stubborn, deceptive, disrespectful, selfish, uncaring, rude, fearful, unhelpful, destructive, spoiled, scheming, moody, feels sorry for himself, deceitful, irresponsible, sarcastic, anxious, greedy, lazy, impatient, rude, lacks self-control, two-faced, sloppy, ungrateful

 # Example

Sample Character Chart for *Andrea Carter and the Long Ride Home*			
Character	Physical Traits	Personality Traits	Likes & Dislikes
Andrea Carter "Andi"	Age 12; youngest daughter of a wealthy ranching family; long, dark hair (usually braided); blue eyes; a few freckles; average height and weight	High-spirited and cheerful; adventurous; friendly; wants to do right, but is impulsive; lacks self-control and patience; loses her temper easily and can be stubborn	Loves horses, especially Taffy; loves the freedom ranch life gives; likes to ride, race, and fish. Dislikes chores; never wants to be a lady
Taffy- Andi's horse	Age 6; golden palomino mare; 15 hands; cream mane/tail; blaze on nose; 4 white socks	A "one-family" horse; smart and loyal; seems to understand Andi's moods	Likes riding with Andi on the range. Dislikes strangers; usually gentle, but reacts wildly when mistreated.
Chad Carter- Andi's brother	Age 26; Black hair, blue eyes; six feet tall, well-muscled; runs the ranch with gusto	Strong-willed and impulsive; quick-tempered, but with a soft heart; clashes with Andi over nearly everything	Loves Andi, but dislikes her irresponsibility regarding his instructions; loves the ranch; has high expectations for his hired hands
Rosa Garduño	Age 12; a Mexican girl Andi meets; long, shiny black hair; dark eyes; a ready smile; part of an immigrant family from Mexico	Shy and quiet, but loves to laugh; hard-working and patient; a steady friend for Andi	Would like to live in one spot instead of being a migrant worker; likes Andi; doesn't like horses much
Felicity Livingston	Age 16; a tall, willowy girl with soft, light brown hair and hazel eyes; only child of a well-to-do rancher	Spoiled and self-willed; a lively girl; quick-witted and sure of herself; has a cruel streak; undisciplined	Likes being in control; hates anyone standing up to her or telling her she is wrong; likes getting her own way

Character Charts

Use these blank charts to take notes about characters you create.

Remember! Make sure your characters have both good and bad traits.

Create your characters!

Watch them come alive!

Character	Physical Traits	Personality Traits (creative imagination, curious, stubborn)	Likes & Dislikes
Spida "Spitsle" meercat	small, 2 months old, VERY hyperactive, very cute, super fast, rarely sleeps	Hates homework, quirky, is youngest in family of 15, so is annoyed alot, and is annoying. does ANYTHING for peanut butter crackers alot like me	Likes his playhouse. Likes a breakfast of fruit loops in front of 100" plasma screen TV. Dislikes Brocolli, celery, and calantro.
Crackers, Spida's older brother	Medium sized, Age !		

More Charts

Create your characters!		Watch them come alive!	
Character	Physical Traits	Personality Traits	Likes & Dislikes

More Charts

Create your characters!		Watch them come alive!	
Character	Physical Traits	Personality Traits	Likes & Dislikes

Put It Together!

Once you have notes about your characters, you can write a character sketch. This is usually a few short paragraphs about your character's physical and personality traits. You do this activity just like you did the warm-up activity about your favorite characters.

Example from my sample chart

Andi Carter is twelve years old and the youngest daughter of a wealthy ranching family in 1880s California. She has long, dark, wavy hair that always gets in the way, so she usually wears it braided. Her eyes are blue.

Andi is high-spirited and friendly. Although she is usually cheerful, she sometimes loses her temper when things aren't going the way she thinks they should. She is adventurous and impulsive, which often gets her into trouble.

Andi loves horses, especially her best friend, Taffy. She likes to ride all over the ranch, and she'll challenge anyone to a horse race. She doesn't like chores and often forgets to do them. She also doesn't like the fact that she is the youngest in her family, and her older brothers and sister are always bossing her around.

Your Character's Name: _____

_____

_____

_____

_____

_____

_____

_____

_____

_____

_____

_____

_____

_____

_____

_____

_____

_____

_____

_____

Another Character's Name: _____

_____

_____

_____

_____

_____

_____

_____

_____

_____

Character Sketches

_____

_____

_____

_____

_____

_____

_____

_____

Another Character's Name: _____

_____

_____

_____

_____

_____

_____

_____

_____

_____

_____

_____

Show-Don't-Tell Feelings

HAPPY, SAD, ANGRY, HURT, SHOCKED

Do you ever have any of these feelings? Of course you do! Everybody has feelings, and your characters must have them, too. It's easy to see what a character in a movie is feeling. You can *see* the feelings. But how does an author show a character's feelings? What do feelings *look* like? Read this sentence:

Paul was very <u>angry</u> when he saw his room.

How can we tell Paul is angry? Is he stamping his feet? Are his fists clenched? What about his face? Is it red? Is he shouting? When you answer these questions using words, you are showing the reader what Paul's anger looks like. Writers always try to: "SHOW—DON'T TELL."

See how Paul shows his anger:

Paul's face turned dark red when he opened the door to his room. He clenched his fists, stomped across the floor, and yelled, "How many times have I told you to stay out of here?"

This shows Paul's anger much better than simply telling the reader that Paul is angry.

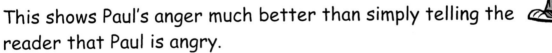

Writer's Hint

If you can't figure out how to show a feeling like "happy" or "sad," it sometimes helps to ask someone to act out the feeling. You can then write down what you see.

What Do Feelings Look Like?

This activity will help you become a good observer of characters' feelings. You need two or more to play. This activity works best when a group can brainstorm about which feeling the "actor" is demonstrating.

Instructions:

1) Cut out the "Feelings" cards on the next page.

2) Fold them up and put them in a bowl

3) One person draws a feeling card from the bowl and acts out the feeling, while the other person (or group) writes down what that feeling looks like.

Use this page to write your feeling words:

_____

_____

_____

_____

_____

_____

_____

_____

_____

_____

_____

Feelings Cards

Cut out these cards to use for the activity

"What Do Feelings Look Like?"

Hungry	Hot	Pain
Cold	Angry	Happy
Sad	Tired/ Bored	Shy
Shocked	Worried	Excited

Characters' Feelings

AFRAID

Hands shaking

Pounding heart

Eyes wide, biting nails

Fast breathing

Whimpering, trembling

HUNGRY

Stomach rumbling

Mouth watering

Smacking lips

Stomach hurting

Sniffing the air

HAPPY

Smiling face

Sparkling eyes

Leaping, clapping

Laughing, twirling

SHOCKED

Mouth wide open

Eyes fly open

Hand over mouth

Gasping

Jumping back

PAIN

Clutching self

Thrashing, rolling

Wailing, teary eyes

Screeching, whimpering

TIRED / BORED

Droopy eyes

Yawning, sighing

Stretching, slouching

Rubbing eyes

SAD

Tears, crying, rubbing eyes

Lips tremble, frowning

Hanging head

Shoulders droop

Dragging feet

EXCITED

Mouth open, eyes wide

Pounding heart

Hands clasped

Jumping, clapping

Yelling, twirling

COLD

Shivering, stamping feet

Rubbing hands

Hugging self

Blowing on hands

Cloudy breath

ANGRY

Red face, glaring

Hands on hips

Stamping feet

Clenched fists

Shouting, breathing hard

Show, Don't Tell!

SHY
Blushing, looking at feet
Arms crossed
Whispering
Standing back
Hunched shoulder

HOT
Red face
Panting
Sweat on face/neck
Drooping
Fanning self with hand

WORRIED
Wringing hands
Biting bottom lip
Stomach flutters
Stuttering
Swallow hard
Heart racing, dry mouth

FRUSTRATED
Crossed arms
Pouting
Tapping foot
Fast breathing
Clenched fists
Outbursts

~Use these blank spaces to add more feeling words~

Guess the Feeling!

Use the feelings chart to identify which emotions the young writers in these examples are showing:

Beth let sobs shake her whole body. She felt the tears running down her face, but she didn't care. She wouldn't believe what she had heard. Her lips started to tremble, and she pulled the pillow up and buried her face in it and screamed. Her eyes got all puffy and red, and she started to cough from all the tears.
~Ashley

FEELING: _____

Lucy Tersil strutted up to Matt and declared, "Your sister will never become a young lady." Matt's whole body stiffened and his throat grew tight. His eyes flashed as he looked her straight in the eyes. ~Alyssa

FEELING: _____

When the day came for the big race, I clasped my hands together and started jumping, clapping, and shouting "Hurray! We're going to a race, hurray!" At last it was 3:00 and it was time to go. I leaped, laughed, and twirled all the way into the van, and on the drive my parents and I all sang songs . . .
~Jacob

FEELING: _____

Wringing her hands, she walked up to the stage. She couldn't get up in front of all those people! She bit her lip, shuffling her feet so it would take a long time to get there. Her stomach felt like it had butterflies flying all around inside. Her heart pounded so hard it felt like it would jump out. She swallowed hard, bit her lip, stumbled up the stairs, and then clenched her fist and pretended to be brave. All the people were looking right at her! She took a deep breath, tried to start her speech, and then, she fainted!   ~Amy

FEELING: _____

Jennie jumped merrily over the log. When she reached the other side she saw a sight that froze her blood. Her eyes flew wide open and she began to shake. Three feet away from her a rattlesnake lay hissing, coiling for a strike. ~Lulu

FEELING: _____

Kit buried her face in her arms, letting out a heavy sigh as she allowed herself to relax for a moment. All too soon she had to sit back up and start reading again, her eyelids drooping. She yawned and rubbed her eyes furiously, trying to focus on the words on the page.   ~Amber   FEELING: _____

It's Your Turn

It's time to practice SHOW—DON'T TELL with your own characters. Follow the steps below. Do this activity over and over. Why? If you can make your character act and think like a real person, you will have a story that touches the reader's own emotions.

1) Choose a feeling from the chart

2) Choose one of the characters you created

3) Think about something that could happen to your character to make him feel this emotion

4) Write 4-6 sentences describing the situation and your character's feelings. Don't use the "feeling" word in the paragraph.

5) Share your writing. Can readers guess which feeling your character is showing?

<u>Telling sentence</u>: Jamie felt <u>cold and miserable</u> waiting in the icy cave.

<u>Showing sentences</u>: Jamie shivered as the icy wind slapped her face. She wrapped her arms around herself and stamped her feet on the frozen ground. Then she sat down, drew a thin blanket around her shoulders, and curled into a tight ball.

<u>Telling sentence</u>: Andi was <u>hungry</u>.

<u>Showing sentence</u>: Andi sat down at the table. Her mouth watered. The smell of hot, buttery rolls set her stomach twisting and growling. She licked her lips and reached for the plate of fried chicken. Then she bit into a drumstick and smiled.

Show--Don't Tell!

Character: _____

Feeling: _____

_____

_____

_____

_____

_____

_____

_____

Character: _____

Feeling: _____

_____

_____

_____

_____

_____

_____

_____

Show-Don't Tell

Character: _____

Feeling: _____

_____

_____

_____

_____

_____

_____

_____

Character: _____

Feeling: _____

_____

_____

_____

_____

_____

_____

_____

_____

For Younger Students

My character's name is: NEB

My character feels: ANGRY

Words that show that feeling: CLENCH FISTS . . .
FACE TURNS RED . . . FAST BREATHING . . .
HANDS ON HIPS . . . SHOUTS . . . STAMP FEET

When the 3 friends would not bow down to the golden idol, King Neb's face turned dark red. He clenched his fists and shouted, "Throw them into the fire!"

******

My character's name is: JONAH

My character feels: AFRAID

Words that show that feeling: HANDS
SHAKE . . . HEART BEATS FAST . . . EYES GET WIDE .
. . CRYING . . .

Jonah sat inside the belly of the fish. His hands shook. His heart beat so fast he could feel it against his chest. It was dark. Jonah started to cry.

For Younger Students

My character's name is:

_____

My character feels: _____

Words that show that feeling: _____

_____

_____

_____

***

_____

_____

_____

_____

_____

_____

_____

_____

For Younger Students

My character's name is:

_____

My character feels: _____

Words that show that feeling: _____

_____

_____

_____

***

_____

_____

_____

_____

_____

_____

_____

_____

Setting and Description

Please don't just tell me the story.
Take me along for the ride.
I'd like to see, and I'd like to be
Traveling right there by your side.

Draw a picture of a "really cool, very awesome, fabulous" ship.

Choose Words Carefully

Compare the drawing of your ship with a friend's. Do they look alike? Did you draw a sailing ship? A steamer? A pirate ship? Maybe you drew a rocket ship. Why don't the pictures look alike?

_____

_____

Your idea of a **REALLY COOL, VERY AWESOME, FABULOUS** ship may not be the same as another writer's idea. A **DELICIOUS** meal for you might be a hamburger, while another writer thinks meatloaf and broccoli are **YUMMY**. The same holds true for **MESSY**. Your mom thinks your room is **MESSY**. You have a different idea when you hear that word.

```
*****************************************************************
             Writer's Hint

  Words that are too general are called DEAD WORDS.
        Seek out and destroy DEAD words!
*****************************************************************
```

Example: A sentence with a dead (general) word:

Her room looked <u>messy</u>.

Instead, use words that paint a picture for the reader:

Her room was exactly as she had left it—the bed unmade, yesterday's school clothes hanging carelessly over a chair, and her nightgown lying in a heap on the floor. Books and papers lay atop her chest of drawers, which stood open. A dusty saddle blanket, discarded in the corner, completed the unappealing scene.

Dead Words

Dead words kill your story faster than anything else. Learn to recognize them. Lasso and round up words that do not paint a picture in your reader's head. Keep the DEAD WORDS in a writing "jail." Let them out only when you absolutely need them. You can add other words to bring life to a dead word. For example: The water was <u>cold</u>. The water was <u>as cold as ice</u>.

DEAD WORD JAIL

All feeling words! awesome   scary   delicious   messy   very   cute   fun   huge   little   awful   terrible   big   gorgeous   beautiful   pretty   great   wonderful   fantastic   fabulous   dirty   boring   good   cool   funny   some   really   yummy   a lot   surprised   marvelous   amazing   strange

~~~~~~

<u>Add more dead words here</u>

_____

_____

_____

_____

_____

_____

_____

_____

_____

It's Your Turn

It's time to take your reader on a tour of a special place in or around your home. It could be your bedroom, a quiet spot in the attic, a special place outdoors, or even the inside of your tent on a camping trip. Show us this place. When you're finished, readers should be able to "see" your special place as if you were showing them a picture.

_____

_____

_____

_____

_____

_____

_____

_____

_____

_____

_____

_____

_____

_____

_____

_____

_____

_____

A Tour Continued...

_____

_____

_____

_____

_____

_____

_____

_____

A Picture

When you finish your writing tour, draw or take a picture of the place you wrote about. Then ask someone to read your description. Does it "look" like the picture?

_____

Go on a Dead Word hunt. How many dead words did you find?

_____

Paste or draw a picture here

Dead Word Hunt

Circle all the DEAD words in the following scene—words that do not paint a picture in your head by SHOWING.

Sarah opened her eyes. It was dark. She lay in bed, wondering what the strange noise was that woke her up. Sarah was nervous. Most of the time she thought she was pretty brave, but not tonight.

The sound came closer. Sarah became more frightened.

Then Sarah felt a really big lump land on her bed. The lump made a very loud noise, and Sarah was terrified! The lump laughed.

Sarah felt foolish. The lump was her awful little brother, playing a dumb joke on her.

****

How many dead words did you find? _____

Sometimes a dead word is not so dead when used with other words. The scene has been rewritten. Read it again. Which dead words did I get rid of? Which dead words did I let "live"?

Sarah opened her eyes. Her room was as black as the inside of a cave. She lay still. *Squeak!* What was that noise? Sarah shivered and squeezed her eyes shut. Most of the time she felt brave, but tonight her heart pounded inside her chest.

Squeak, squeak, squeak! The sound was coming closer! Sarah's breath came in quick gasps. She felt a trickle of sweat run down the back of her neck.

A lump the size of a wolf pounced on her bed. "Grrrrrr," the lump shouted. Sarah screamed. The lump laughed.

Sarah felt her face turn red. She clenched her fists. The lump was not a wolf. "Go away, Peter!" Sarah hollered at her little brother.

Writing Cameras

When you took the reader on a tour of a special room or place, you were using an imaginary Writing Camera inside your head. Just like a real camera, a Writing Camera **freezes** the scene so the reader can see, hear, touch, smell, and taste what you, the author, want them to experience. When you take a Writing Snapshot, you draw the reader's attention to important characters, settings, and objects in your story, using vivid details.

****
Writer's Hint

Don't go crazy with your writing camera and freeze (describe) every scene! Take a writing snapshot of the KEY (the most important) **CHARACTERS**, **SETTINGS**, and **OBJECTS** that move the story along.
****

Study the following examples to learn how you can change boring "telling" sentences into vibrant "snapshots" with your writing camera.

Before: The storm was <u>very bad.</u>
After: Lightning flashed across the sky. Thunder exploded. The wind whipped branches from the trees and sent them scuttling through the forest.

Before: Paul opened his gift, and out jumped a <u>really cute</u> puppy.
After: A golden puppy leaped from the box and into Paul's arms. Long, floppy ears, soft as silk, brushed Paul's cheeks. A quick, wet tongue gave him a puppy kiss.

Before: Michael's science project was <u>really awesome!</u>
After: Red, yellow, and green sparks flew from Michael's science project. A motor hummed, and the metal contraption zoomed across the table. It flew over the edge, onto the floor, and kept on rolling—right out the door.

It's Your Turn

Use your imaginary writing camera to turn these "telling" sentences into writing snapshots that "show" the reader the scene.

Before: Our camping trip was boring because it rained all week.

After: _____

_____

_____

_____

_____

_____

_____

_____

Before: Katie saw a scary sea creature at the aquarium.

After: _____

_____

_____

_____

_____

_____

_____

_____

_____

One More Time!

This time you are going to write a longer scene. Take your Writing Camera and enter a cave, where an ancient treasure chest lies, waiting to be discovered. Describe the chest and its contents, and your adventure, if you like!

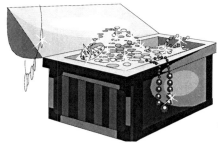

★★★

Writer's Hint

Don't know what to write? Here are some questions to ask yourself when using your writing camera:

1) What color? How big?

2) What does it feel like?

3) Does it make any sounds?

4) Size? Shape?

5) Does it have a taste? What kind?

6) Is there a smell? What kind?

7) Temperature? Hot? Cold?

★★★

Before: When I entered the cave, I found the object of my search—the lost treasure chest of the Ancients.

After: _____

_____

_____

_____

_____

_____

_____

_____

Too Many Snapshots?

What kind of pictures do you take when you go on a trip? Do you take a picture of your suitcase or your plane ticket? Of course not!

Why not? _____

If you wrote that a snapshot of your suitcase and the plane ticket are not the important or interesting parts of the trip, you're right.

****
Writer's Hint

A writing camera freezes the action, which means your story is frozen, also. Remember to take snapshots of **KEY** characters, settings, and objects only! Use your writing camera carefully!
****

The story below includes details about KEY characters, settings, and objects. Unfortunately, the writer went a little crazy with her writing camera and also took some extra "snapshots" of characters, settings, or objects that are *not* important. Can you find the details that should be left out? Cross out the details that are not KEY to moving the story along.

Little Red Riding Hood lived with her 30-year-old mother in a small cottage in the woods. Ivy climbed and weaved around the cottage. One day she set out to bring her grandmother a basket of food. Mother packed a fresh loaf of bread, a few slices of bologna, and a thermos of hot, steaming cocoa in the basket. Red Riding Hood left the cottage and wandered along the path through the deep, dark forest. Her stomach fluttered at the shadows. Suddenly, from behind a tall fir tree, a dark, shaggy creature with pointed ears and a mouth full of sharp teeth appeared. It was a wolf!

Do You Agree?

Here is the same story. I underlined the unnecessary details.

Little Red Riding Hood lived with her **30-year-old** mother in a small cottage in the woods. **Ivy climbed and weaved around the cottage**. One day she set out to bring her grandmother a basket of food. **Mother packed a fresh loaf of bread, a few slices of bologna, and a thermos of hot, steaming cocoa in the basket.** Red Riding Hood left the cottage and wandered along the path through the deep, dark forest. Her stomach fluttered at the shadows. Suddenly, from behind a tall fir tree, a dark, shaggy creature with pointed ears and a mouth full of sharp teeth. It was a wolf!

Why?

30-year-old: Do we need to know how old Red Riding Hood's mother is? No!

Ivy climbed and weaved around the cottage. This has nothing to do with what is going to happen in the story.

Mother packed a fresh loaf of bread, a few slices of bologna, and a thermos of hot, steaming cocoa in the basket. Nice, but it slows the story down. It doesn't really matter what is in the basket.

However, since Red Riding Hood is a **KEY** character, it is important to see what she sees and to feel what she is feeling as she heads for Grandma's. So I kept the details about her trip through the woods and her meeting with the wolf.

It's Your Turn

Learning to use a Writing Camera is so important that I've included extra activities so you can practice this skill. A writing camera is perfect for SHOWING—NOT TELLING your characters' feelings as well as the settings and objects in your story.

<u>Assignment #1</u>- Find a picture of an interesting character (animals work well), an object, or an unusual setting (like a castle or a space station). Now write a word picture to describe it. Check the DEAD WORD jail to make sure you are not using dead words. Focus on vivid details. When you finish, ask someone to read your word picture and see if it matches the picture.

_____

_____

_____

_____

_____

_____

_____

_____

Paste or draw picture here

_____

_____

_____

_____

Assignment #2- Follow these steps:

1- Choose a character from your character chart.

2- Choose one of the settings listed below.

3- Use your Writing Camera and your Feelings Chart to put your character in the setting. Take a snapshot. Show us your character in action. What does he/she see? What does he do? What is he/she feeling? Make us feel like we are right there.

~Fishing in the creek on a summer's day

~Romping through a field of flowers

~Exploring a planet with two suns

~Sitting in a tree house during a rainstorm

~Lying on a sandy beach

~Sitting on a hilltop on a starry night

~Commanding a spaceship during a battle

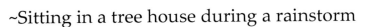

~Lying in the hospital with a broken arm

~Standing at the school drinking fountain with a bully

~Scuba diving at the bottom of the ocean

~Waiting on the baseball diamond just before you're up to bat

~Hiking through a dark forest

~Exploring an old castle

~ _____ (Your idea)

CHARACTER: _____

SETTING: _____

_____

_____

_____

_____

_____

_____

_____

_____

CHARACTER: _____

SETTING: _____

_____

_____

_____

_____

_____

_____

_____

_____

_____

CHARACTER: _____

SETTING: _____

_____

_____

_____

_____

_____

_____

_____

CHARACTER: _____

SETTING: _____

_____

_____

_____

_____

_____

_____

_____

_____

CHARACTER: _____

SETTING: _____

_____

_____

_____

_____

_____

_____

_____

CHARACTER: _____

SETTING: _____

_____

_____

_____

_____

_____

_____

_____

_____

_____

Sentence Variety

Sometimes when you are looking for words that show-don't-tell, the sentences all start sounding alike. For example, this paragraph shows Sandy being shy. The word choices show her shyness, but the sentences start the same way. They all look alike.

Sandy blushed when Peter came up and stood next to her. **She** hid her face and looked down. **She** shuffled her feet. **She** was gulping and hanging her head.

By adding a few extra words, you can give your sentences variety.

Sandy blushed when Peter came up. Quickly, she turned away. "What does he want?" she wondered. Her feet shuffled. They seemed to have a mind of their own. Huge gulps made her swallow hard. She wished Peter would go away.

The same thing holds true for freezing scenes with your writing camera. When you take a writing picture, do all your sentences start the same way?

My cat is black and white. **She has** fur as soft as a fuzzy chick. **She has** four paws and a tail about twelve inches long. **She has** five whiskers on each side of her cold, black nose. **She has** a pink tongue.

This is a good word picture, with vivid details. However, it is a little boring to read because all the sentences sound alike. Here's the rewrite:

My special cat, Frisky, is black and white. **Her fur** is as soft as a fuzzy chick. **When she runs**, her four white paws barely touch the ground. **A long, black tail** about twelve inches long twitches whenever she sees a bird. **Her whiskers** twitch, too. **The whiskers** on one side of her face are black. The other whiskers are white. **She likes to lick** me with her rough, pink tongue.

It's Your Turn

If you're having trouble using variety in your sentences, then this page is for you! Choose one of these paragraphs to rewrite, using variety. Add extra words. Use your imagination.

1) Brian leaped into the air. **He opened** his mouth and shouted. **He clapped** his hands. **He ran** around in circles, laughing and yelling. His heart pounded.

2) My stuffed horse is about eight inches long. **It has** four brown hooves with white socks. **It has** a long, fluffy black tail about three inches long. **It has** two beady eyes and a stripe down its nose. **It has** a white mane that sticks up.

_____

_____

_____

_____

_____

_____

_____

_____

_____

_____

_____

_____

Story Beginnings--the Hook

There's just one chance to "hook" your reader;
Just one! Not six or nine.
Make sure when you start, that you do your part
To keep readers attached to your "line."

Have you ever gone fishing? If so, what do you need if you plan to catch a fish? Yep, a fishing pole, a hook, and some decent bait: salmon eggs, flies, spinners, worms, herring. Every fisherman knows you can't hook a fish if you use the wrong bait, or dried-up bait, or worse—no bait! You won't catch a 30-pound salmon with a worm, nor will you catch a rainbow trout with a herring.

Writing stories is a lot like fishing. The author needs to use the right kind of "bait" to hook readers. And when should you catch your readers? On the very first page of your story! Just like a good fisherman carefully chooses his bait to snag a fish, you, the author, must hook your reader with a smashing beginning. Once you catch your reader, you can reel him in with your real-life characters and your excellent use of your writing camera.

Read the beginnings of a few books. How did the author catch your interest (or not)?

_____

_____

_____

_____

Hook Your Reader

Just like there are different kinds of bait for different kinds of fish, there are different techniques an author can use to capture the reader's interest. Begin your story with a few "grabber" sentences that "hook" the reader.

I've discovered seven kinds of "bait" that work well:

1) Action   2) Dialogue   3) an Unusual Setting   4) a Thought or Feeling

5) a Question   6) an Interesting Character   7) a Sound Effect.

Each technique (bait) on the following two pages shows an example of how it is used to make a good impression in the first few sentences of your story.

Cut out the cards, mount them on cardstock, and match the bait with the example. Store your cards in a pocket you can make by gluing a small piece of cardstock here.

[place pocket here]

Seven Ways to Hook Your Reader

In addition to these cards, there is a reference guide for all seven techniques on page 75.

Dialogue 	"Will they come back?" Tina whispered. She looked at her brother for an answer. "I don't know," Peter said. "I hope not." He dropped down from the attic window and fell onto a mattress lying in the corner. "But what if they do?" Tina asked. "What if they search the attic next time? Where will we hide?"
Action 	Too late Jason saw it—the huge, gaping blackness blocking his path. He dug his heels into the soft ground and tried to stop his headlong flight. No good. The darkness engulfed him with one giant bite, and Jason found himself falling . . . falling . . . falling into a hole that seemed to have no end.
Unusual Setting 	The cave was dark and dripping wet from last night's high tide. Seaweed clung to the low ceiling, giving off a salty scent. A crab scuttled across the sand-covered floor, its claws and legs rustling. At the back of the cave, behind a massive outcropping covered with orange and lavender starfish, a half-rotten lifeboat waited. It wasn't just any lifeboat. This lifeboat had a story to tell—to anyone unlucky enough to discover its hiding place.

Thought or Feeling

It all started with Zach—like it usually does. I mean, he's my best friend and all (and friends are hard to come by in the middle of outer space, so I'm not too particular), but sometimes he can be a real pain. He thinks because my father's the commander of the station, I can get access to all kinds of "off-limits" areas, but that is totally not true.

A Question

Now what do I do? Ty glanced at the tangle of wires, microchips, circuit boards, and pieces of metal lying in a heap on his worktable. Then he glanced at the clock. *Two hours.* Not enough time. *What am I going to tell Mr. Sandberg when he arrives?*

Interesting Character

"You'd better not let Miss W. catch you blubbering."

Julie jerked her head from the pillow and glanced up. Staring down at her was the face of a girl just about her own age, with green eyes and bright red, curly hair. It was done up in two pigtails that stuck out from her head in wild tangles. A multitude of freckles covered her nose and round cheeks. The girl blew a huge bubble of gum, which popped. Pink splattered her face. She grinned. "I'm Ashley. You the new arrival?"

Sound Effect

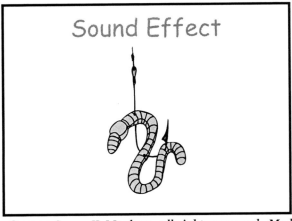

Beep, beep, beep . . .

Samantha jerked awake. Her hand crashed down on the alarm clock.

Beep, beep, beep . . .

Another whack. Then silence.

Samantha looked at the time: 3:04 a.m. *Perfect*, she thought. Then she snatched her cell phone from the nightstand and began dialing the number.

Seven Ways to Hook Your Reader

BAIT	EXAMPLE
Dialogue	"Will they come back?" Tina whispered. She looked at her brother for an answer. "I don't know," Peter said. "I hope not." He dropped down from the attic window and fell onto a mattress lying in the corner. "But what if they do?" Tina asked. "What if they search the attic next time? Where will we hide?"
Action	Too late Jason saw it—the huge, gaping blackness blocking his path. He dug his heels into the soft ground and tried to stop his headlong flight. No good. The darkness engulfed him with one giant bite, and Jason found himself falling . . . falling . . . falling into a hole that seemed to have no end.
An Unusual Setting	The cave was dark and dripping wet from last night's high tide. Seaweed clung to the low ceiling, giving off a salty scent. A crab scuttled across the sand-covered floor, its claws and legs rustling. At the back of the cave, behind a massive outcropping covered with orange and lavender starfish, a half-rotten lifeboat waited. It wasn't just any lifeboat. This lifeboat had a story to tell—to anyone unlucky enough to discover its hiding place.
A Thought or Feeling	It all started with Zach—like it usually does. I mean, he's my best friend and all (and friends are hard to come by in the middle of outer space, so I'm not too particular), but sometimes he can be a real pain. He thinks because my father's the commander of the station, I can get access to all kinds of "off-limits" areas, but that is totally not true.
A Question	*Now what do I do?* Ty glanced at the tangle of wires, microchips, circuit boards, and pieces of metal lying in a heap on his worktable. Then he glanced at the clock. *Two hours.* Not enough time. *What am I going to tell Mr. Sandberg when he arrives?*
Interesting Character	"You'd better not let Miss W. catch you blubbering." Julie jerked her head from the pillow and glanced up. Staring down at her was the face of a girl just about her own age, with green eyes and bright red, curly hair. It was done up in two pigtails that stuck out from her head in wild tangles. A multitude of freckles covered her nose and round cheeks. The girl blew a huge bubble of gum, which popped. Pink splattered her face. She grinned. "I'm Ashley. You the new arrival?"
A Sound Effect	*Beep, beep, beep . .* Samantha jerked awake. Her hand crashed down on the alarm clock. *Beep, beep, beep . . .* Another whack. Then silence. Samantha looked at the clock: 3:04 a.m. *Perfect,* she thought. Then she snatched her cell phone from the nightstand and began dialing the number.

Boring Beginnings

Now that you've seen some good examples of ways to hook your reader, let's see if you can change some boring beginnings into tasty "bait."

```
****************************************************************
*                     Writer's Hint                           *
*                                                              *
*  The KEY to writing fiction is: Create a character           *
*  with a problem he must solve, and give him some-            *
*  thing interesting to do in order to solve it. Start         *
*                your story with a bang!                       *
****************************************************************
```

Here are some opening sentences that might cause a reader to toss your story aside. Would you want to keep reading these stories?

<u>Assignment:</u> Each boring, opening sentence below has been changed to a more exciting "hook" on the next page. Can you see the difference and match them up? (The first one has been done for you).

1) This story is about the time Brian got a chemistry set for his birthday.

2) One day last week an outlaw stole Jack's horse.

3) Tina and Peter liked to solve mysteries.

4) Samantha went to school, and the teacher yelled at her again.

5) One day Sarah woke up and decided to look out her window.

6) I want to tell you about my adventures on a space station.

7) Hi. My name is Jamie. I am ten years old and I like spiders.

8) One time a rocket ship landed on a planet with two suns.

9) Mary was always in trouble.

10) Anna heard a scary noise and wondered what it was.

You can use these hooks not only to begin your story but also to begin each chapter in a longer book. Each chapter is like a mini-story.

Technique to use	Examples
Dialogue	"Come back here with my horse!" Jack shouted. The outlaw laughed. "Come and catch him, if you can."
Dialogue	**1** "It's here! It arrived today." Brian ran for the door and jerked it open. "This for you, kid?" The deliveryman thrust a heavy, oddly-shaped package into Brian's hands.
Action	Sara awoke and leaped from her bed. She ran to the window, threw open the curtains, and gasped.
A Question	"Will they come back?" Tina whispered. She looked at her brother for an answer. "I don't know," Peter said. "I hope not."
A Question	What—Mary asked herself—was the point of trying to be good, when nobody really cared about her?
Thought or Feeling	It all started with Zach—like it usually does. I mean, he's my best friend (and friends are hard to come by in the middle of outer space, so I'm not too particular), but sometimes he can be a real pain.
Thought or Feeling	Jamie loved spiders. Especially the big, hairy ones.
A Character	Samantha folded her arms across her chest, squinted, and snapped her gum—daring the teacher to scold her.
Unusual Setting	The double-suns of Epsilon 5 rose, blood-red, over the jagged mountains, casting an eerie shadow behind the ship.
Sound Effect	*Scratch, scratch, scratch.* There it was again. Anna pulled the covers over her head and shivered. What could it be?

It's Your Turn

Can you guess which techniques these authors used to "hook" a reader?

There is no one right answer. Some may have more than one hook.

~I am afraid. Someone is coming. That is, I think someone is coming, and I pray that I am wrong. ~*Z for Zachariah* by Robert C. O'Brien **Hook**: _____

~In the last days of Narnia, far up the west beyond Lantern Waste and close beside the great waterfall, there lived an Ape. He was so old that no one could remember when he had first come to live in those parts, and he was the cleverest, ugliest, most wrinkled Ape you can imagine ~*The Last Battle* by C. S. Lewis **Hook**:_____

~It happened so quickly, so unexpectedly, that Little Jon's cry was almost instantly cut short as the blackness closed over him. No one knew the hole was there. It hadn't been there the day before, and in the twilight no one noticed it. ~*The Forgotten Door* by Alexander Key **Hook**:_____

~"Cluck, cluck, cluck!" TJ Stenson glanced toward the source of the chicken imitation and quickly looked away. He wished the after-school activities bus would hurry. Why was it always late on the days when Craig Ackerley decided to hassle him? "Cluck, cluck, cluck, CLUCK. Cluck CLUCK!" TJ ignored him. ~*Night of Fear* by Peg Kehret

Hook: _____

~When twelve-year-old Andrea Carter brought her golden palomino mare to a skidding halt near her favorite fishing spot, she expected to find a bubbling, splashing creek full of trout just waiting to be snatched up for supper. Instead, she found a dead man. ~*Andrea Carter and the Family Secret* by Susan K. Marlow

Hook: _____

~"Little Man, would you come on? You keep it up and you're gonna make us late." My youngest brother paid no attention to me. ~*Roll of Thunder, Hear My Cry* by Mildred D. Taylor **Hook**: _____

~Way cool! Me, Dakota Anderson, humming down the road beside my dad in his brand-new red Ferrari! I sank into the leather seat, breathing in the new car smell and squinting against the sun's rays shooting off the hood. ~*Out at Home* by Jeannie St. John Taylor **Hook**: _____

Practice

You (or another character) are walking along the beach when you discover a lifeboat that has washed ashore. Using what you've learned, begin a story that HOOKS your reader, so they want to keep reading.

Here are examples of how this can be done. I only wrote a couple of sentences. You should write at least a paragraph.

Action: Samantha saw it first. She tumbled down the side of the sand dune, raced across the beach, and nearly fell into the gray, weather-beaten lifeboat.

Dialogue: "Come quick!" Samantha squealed when she saw the lifeboat. "Look what last night's storm washed up."

Question-thought-feeling: Samantha stopped short when she found the lifeboat, half buried in the sand. *What's that?* Her eyes widened, and a warm glow spread to her fingertips. *It's all mine,* she thought. *I found it first, and nobody better take it away!*

Sound effect: *Crash!* The waves tossed the old, abandoned lifeboat against the rocks with a force that splintered the ancient wood.

Unusual setting: The cave was dark, and dripping wet from last night's high tide. Behind a rock covered with orange and lavender starfish, a half-rotten lifeboat waited. It wasn't just any lifeboat. This lifeboat had a story to tell—to anyone unlucky enough to discover its hiding place.

On the next page is your chance to write a HOOK for this story beginning.

A Lifeboat Story

Action * Dialogue * Unusual Setting

Sound Effect * A Question * Thought or Feeling
Interesting Character

Circle the hook or "hooks" you used to begin the lifeboat story.

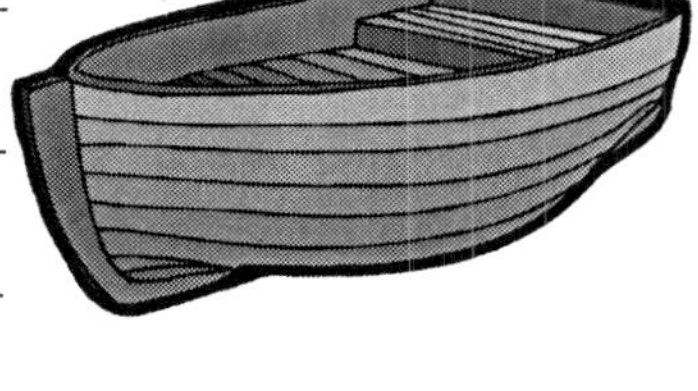

Begin Your Story

Are you ready to start your own story? You've created your characters, showed their feelings, and put them in a setting. You have had an opportunity to brainstorm, and hopefully you have come up with an idea. Do you remember the KEY to writing fiction? If not, look back in this book. Fill in the blanks:

****

The Key to Writing Fiction is:

Create a _____ with a

_____ he must solve, and give him

something _____ to do in

order to _____ it.

****

There are more elements (pieces) that go into a story, but you should have enough to write a beginning that will grab your readers. Have you thought of a title for your story? If so, write it here:

_____

The best way to write a story is to type it into a writing program on the computer. It is easy to make changes, switch things around, delete, and use the spell-check feature. If you prefer to write your story in *Reach for the Stars*, you will find plenty of pages at the back of the book for this purpose. Check them out and write your beginning!

Story Glue

There are 5 elements of a fiction story, but what holds the pieces together? Story glue!

Before we talk about story glue, do you remember the five elements of a fiction story? Write them here from memory:

_____

_____

_____

_____

_____

The five elements need glue to hold the story together and make it read smoothly. Things like dialogue (people talking), ups and downs (conflict), point of view (who's telling the story?), and nutshell summaries (what's the story all about?) keep your story's "puzzle pieces" together to create a final, satisfying story.

Nutshell Summaries

You can have a fantastic beginning,
And characters who make readers care;
But without a PLOT, you haven't GOT
Much of a story to share.

This lesson focuses on "Nutshell Summaries" . . . or . . . "What's Your Point?" Your story must have a plot—a purpose. Otherwise it's in danger of falling into the B category (Boring). When you can take your story idea and summarize it in one or two sentences (just enough to stuff into a walnut shell), then you have created a Nutshell Summary.

A catalog description of a book is a fantastic way to see how a plot is summarized. Here are nutshell summaries for some great stories:

Fleischman, *By the Great Horn Spoon:* To save his sister's home, young Jack and his butler rush off to California to join the '49ers in their hunt for gold.

Lewis, C.S., *The Horse and His Boy:* A talking horse and a servant-boy save Narnia from invasion.

Tolkien, *The Hobbit:* Bilbo Baggins sets out to help the dwarves reclaim their home and treasures in the Lonely Mountain from an evil dragon.

Sperry, *Call it Courage:* Mafatu, the son of a Great Chief of Polynesia, overcomes his fear of the sea and proves he isn't a coward.

Brady, Esther Wood, *Toliver's Secret:* Ten-year-old Ellen Toliver must conquer her timidity to take a secret message through enemy lines during the Revolutionary War.

Nutshell Summaries

If you remember this . . .

. . . then you can do this!

Example:

Wrong way (past tense):

Andi's poor choices <u>plunged</u> her into danger when she <u>took</u> her horse Taffy and <u>left</u> her home on the Circle C ranch.

Right way (present tense):

Andi's poor choices <u>plunge</u> her into danger when she <u>takes</u> her horse Taffy and <u>leaves</u> her home on the Circle C ranch.

It's Your Turn

Think of your favorite books or even your favorite movies/videos. Can you come up with a one or two-sentence "nutshell" for each? Remember that summaries are short, sweet, and to the point, without "hooks" or details, and are in the present tense.

Title:

Nutshell Summary: _____

_____

_____

_____

_____

Title:

Nutshell Summary: _____

_____

_____

_____

_____

Title:

Nutshell Summary: _____

_____

_____

_____

_____

Vote!

The following nutshell summaries come from actual students' story ideas. What do you think? Are they good examples or not? Why or why not?

When Jo's pony gets stolen, she sets off to find it and then gets lost in the Wild West in Australia. How can she survive?   ~ Beth

_____

_____

_____

Life was already tough for two teens, but when they have to separate and Vikings attack, they can no longer lean on each other, but on God.   ~Rachel

_____

_____

_____

When Jennie O'Neal and her family move from Ireland to far-off America, Jennie must learn to cope with the trials of a new environment, a new home, and new enemies. ~Lulu

_____

_____

_____

Katie and Jen find a life boat one day that contains a boy, his younger sister, and a treasure map. They immediately set out for adventure.   ~ Vera Faye

_____

_____

_____

Four teens are mysteriously transported into a world called Dargothia. Teaming up with two of the inhabitants, they try to stop a war and bring the Dargothian people back together, and maybe find a way home.   ~Danielle

_____

_____

Your Story's Nutshell

Can you write a nutshell summary for *your* story? Here are three boxes for nutshell summaries for stories you create.

Title:

Nutshell Summary: _____

_____

_____

_____

_____

Title:

Nutshell Summary: _____

_____

_____

_____

_____

Title:

Nutshell Summary: _____

_____

_____

_____

_____

Dialogue

Dialogue between characters
Is a must for successful scenes.
It moves the plot, and you learn a lot
About the hero's hopes and dreams.

Dialogue simply means "characters talking to each other." Sometimes the main characters talk to themselves, too, in thoughts. But there's a lot more to writing dialogue than simply giving characters something to say. Here are a few hints for writing good dialogue:

Hint #1- Quotation Marks

Use quotation marks to show a character is speaking. Quotation marks look like this: " " Put these marks around what the character is saying. The periods, commas, question marks, and exclamation points go inside the quotation marks.

"What time is it?"   "I'm coming," she said. "My cat is missing!"   "I like chocolate."

Don't use quotation marks for thoughts: *I wish I could fly*, Sarah thought.

Hint #2- Tags

Use "tags" to identify the speakers, unless the reader can easily figure out who is talking. "Tags" are words like: he said, she answered, Johnny shouted, Mary replied, Philip whispered, Susie muttered, he called, they yelled. Fill in the "tags" for the examples below:

Mother stood on the porch and _____, "Connie! Come in now!"

"Do I have to?" Connie _____.

"Yes," Mother _____. "It's getting dark. I don't want you out there."

Connie scuffed her shoe in the dirt. "But I'm just starting to have fun."

"Hurry up!" Mother _____.

Hint #3- Indent

When a new character starts talking, indent (make a new paragraph). If you run all of the conversation together, nobody will be able to figure out who is saying what!

"Batter-up! We haven't got all day!" Tom shouted. "Stop yelling," Katie said. She grabbed the bat and scowled at her brother. He scowled back. "No girls," Sean piped up from the pitcher's mound. "What do you care? She's not on your team," Tom snapped. Sean glared at Katie for a moment, then shrugged. "Suit yourself. But I'm not going easy on her just 'cause she's a girl." "Who's asking you to?" Katie said. "Play ball!"

Indent!

    "Batter up! We haven't got all day!" Tom shouted.

   "Stop yelling," Katie said. She grabbed the bat and scowled at her brother. He scowled back.

   "No girls," Sean piped up from the pitcher's mound.

   "What do you care? She's not on your team," Tom snapped.

   Sean glared at Katie for a moment then shrugged. "Suit yourself. But I'm not going easy on her just 'cause she's a girl."

   "Who's asking you to?" Katie said. "Play ball!"

Hint #4- No Empty Chatter!

Use dialogue to move the plot along or to tell the reader something important about the characters. Don't write empty chatter. Just like your "writing camera" takes snapshots of KEY characters, settings, and objects, your dialogue should be about things that matter. Readers don't want to read pages of dialogue with no purpose.

Hint #5- Mix It Up!

Pages of dialogue alone get boring. Sprinkle your characters' speaking with actions, feelings, description, and narration. Move that story along!

Dialogue Detective

Here's a conversation between Lucy and the Faun, Mr. Tumnus, from *The Lion, the Witch, and the Wardrobe.* Is it easy to read? _____
Why or why not? _____

With a red pencil, underline everything Lucy is saying.
With a green pencil, underline everything Mr. Tumnus is saying.

"No, I'm a bad Faun. I don't suppose there ever was a worse Faun since the beginning of the world." "But what have you done?" "My old father, now, that's his picture over the mantelpiece. He would never have done a thing like this." "A thing like what?" "Like what I've done. Taken service under the White Witch. That's what I am. I'm in the pay of the White Witch." "The White Witch? Who's she?" "Why, it is she that has got all Narnia under her thumb. It's she that makes it always winter. Always winter and never Christmas. Think of that!" "How awful!"

(If you said it was hard to read because there are no "tags" and the paragraphs have not been indented, you are correct.)

On the next page, copy the conversation and do these two things:
1) Indent (make a new paragraph) each time Lucy or Mr. Tumnus talks.
2) Put in dialogue "tags" so the reader can tell who is speaking. If you want to use the same tags the author, C.S. Lewis, used, find a copy of the book and peek at this conversation in Chapter Two. But it's not required. Use whatever tags you think will make it clear.

It's Your Turn

Creating a Scene

A scene is a main event that occurs in the story. Each scene usually has a beginning, a middle, and an end. Some short stories are only one scene long. A novel (or a movie) is a series of scenes, each one linked together and building in intensity, until the climax (most important event) of the story.

Writer's Hint #1

A well-written scene includes:

~ACTION~

~DIALOGUE~

~CONFLICT~

~FEELINGS~

~DESCRIPTION~

Writer's Hint #2

A scene is a "mini-story" inside of a longer story.

Writer's Hint #3

Each chapter of a novel is often a complete scene.

Not every scene must use *every* element from Writer's Hint #1. On the next page is an example of a well-written scene, created by a student from my writing workshop. It is a short chapter from what could be a longer book about a girl adventurer.

Which three elements did this author use in her chapter scene?

_____ _____ _____

Which two elements did she not use?

_____ _____

Here is the "nutshell" summary of this scene:

An adventurer discovers an ancient chest in a secret cave.

I was feeling less like Indiana Jones with every move. And less like a girl who had studied for years about this long-lost chest I was after. I army-crawled into the low, pitch-black cleft in the rock. "A cave," my informer had called it. I scoffed yet again at those words as the space got even narrower.

I held my flashlight between my neck and shoulder as I squeezed between the rocks that seemed about to make me the ham of a sandwich. My elbows were scraped raw, and my pants were ripped. Sweat dripped on the dirt and gravel I crawled across. Slow going. The space was now too narrow for me to wrestle through. I shook my backpack off and tossed it in front of me, pushing it ahead whenever I caught up with it. I was flat on my gut, shimmying into what was probably a dead end—like all my other expeditions.

My fedora scraped off, and there was no turning around to get it. *Great. There goes the last of my Indiana Jones spirit.*

After an hour of crawling, I pushed myself out of the tunnel and into a vast opening as large and empty as a warehouse that had been cleared out. I whooshed out a sigh of relief to have my feet under me and said aloud,

"Now *this* is a cave!"

My voice echoed many times off the walls until the sound finally dissolved into the air. I ran my flashlight across the walls, where hieroglyphic figures were painted in colorful detail. I could read some of them, but I wasn't interested in try-ing to sort it all out right then. I had a treasure to find.

Pulling the compass out of my bulky pack, I found the north side of the cave and ran my fingers over the paintings on the rock wall. I couldn't bear to smash them with a chisel. I knew they were important pieces of history that would be de-molished. Despite my hurry, I took out my camera and snapped several pictures and drew the signs in a notebook, in case the pictures were no good. Closing my eyes, I brought my chisel down and connected with rock, sending shards flying. Whew, this was going to take awhile . . .

A long time later—I still don't know how long, I laid aside my chisel and brought out the more detailed archeology tools. My heart raced as I forced my hands not to shake. Finally, it was out of the mountain. The chest I had searched for, for ten years, was in my hands.

Now, to open it.   ~by Maegan, *used with permission*

It's Your Turn

You are writing a story about searching for treasure in the jungles of South America. At one point in the story, your characters end up on a raft in the river, heading for the rapids. Here is a "nutshell" summary of that one scene (or chapter):

Josh and his friends ride the rapids on a leaky raft and survive.

You may use different character names, a boat instead of a raft, natives can chase them, they can go over a waterfall, or wherever your imagination takes you. But remember, your scene needs a beginning, a middle, and an end, as well as scene elements from Writer's Hint #1 (page 92). Turn the nutshell summary into a scene by using some of these hints:

ACTION: gripping the edge of the raft, nearly overturning the raft, grabbing at branches, paddling, running from natives, crashing into rocks

DIALOGUE: the main character shouting instructions, what the characters might say to each other

CONFLICT: natives chasing, arguing characters

FEELINGS/THOUGHTS: what the characters are thinking, SHOW how they feel—fear, panic

DESCRIPTION: of the raft, river, natives, sounds of the river, waterfall, (think: writing camera)

****
REMINDER!

YOU DON'T NEED TO USE
EVERY ELEMENT IN
YOUR SCENE.
****

Create a Scene

_____

_____

_____

_____

_____

_____

_____

_____

_____

_____

_____

_____

_____

_____

_____

_____

_____

_____

_____

_____

_____

_____

Create a Scene

Now choose another nutshell summary from below . . . OR . . . Create a scene for the story you are writing. Jot down notes about the different elements you want to include in the scene. Then write the scene on the next page. Have fun!

~I hit a homerun and won the game for our team.
~On the fishing trip, Riley caught the biggest trout of all!
~I tripped and spilled the special cake I baked.
~Jamie stood up to the bully at the drinking fountain.

~Nutshell summary of a scene from your own story:

_____

_____

_____

ACTION: _____

_____

DIALOGUE: _____

_____

CONFLICT: _____

_____

FEELINGS/THOUGHTS: _____

_____

DESCRIPTION: _____

_____

Create a Scene

Note: If you are creating a scene for your own story, you may wish to write it on the computer or as part of your ongoing story on the story pages at the back of this book.

_____

_____

_____

_____

_____

_____

_____

_____

_____

_____

_____

_____

_____

_____

_____

_____

_____

_____

_____

_____

_____

_____

Create a Scene

_____
_____
_____
_____
_____
_____
_____
_____
_____
_____
_____
_____
_____
_____
_____
_____
_____
_____
_____
_____
_____
_____

Point of View

Who's telling this story, anyway?
The hero? The bad guy? Or you?
Make it clear if you can, readers *must* understand
The story from *ONE* point of view!

Stories are not like TV shows. In a TV show or a movie like *Narnia*, first we see what's happening with Lucy and the wardrobe, then we switch scenes to the White Witch and Edmund, and then we jump to the enemy camp or Aslan or the girls. Many adult books switch points of view (POV), but it is difficult for young authors to keep the story straight for their readers if they jump around between characters.

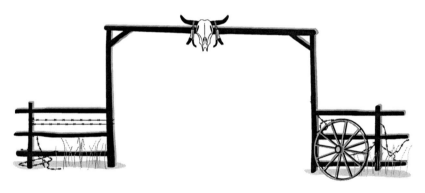

The old saying, "Meanwhile, back at the ranch," doesn't work well in most stories. It's best to follow your main character around. If he stays on the ship, keep your reader there. If he goes back to the ranch, then go with him. Don't leave him trapped at the bottom of the sea while you tell the story from another character's viewpoint.

****
Writer's Hint

Decide who your main character is, and tell the entire story from his or her (or its) point of view. If you **must** change points of view, do it with a new chapter or with a scene break.
****

Point of View

To help you understand what this means, read the following scene, which has been written TWICE—once from the young girl's point of view, and the second time around from her older brother's point of view.

#1-   Without warning, the enormous animal reared up and screamed a challenge . . . Andi's mind shouted, *Jump down!* But she couldn't move. Her arms and legs were frozen with fear . . . An instant later, she found herself flying backward through the air. She landed in the dust with a painful *thud* and heard a tremendous *crack.* The stallion's hooves connected with the corral fence and brought it tumbling down.

Andi lay on the ground a few yards from the corral and tried to catch her breath . . . She had no idea how she'd managed to escape . . . She glanced around the yard. It was suddenly alive with activity . . .

A shadow fell across her, and Andi looked up. Chad towered over her, hands on his hips, glaring. She had never seen her brother so furious.... "What were you doing?" he bellowed. "You could have been killed!"

~From *Andrea Carter and the Long Ride Home* by Susan K. Marlow

In the first example, we see, hear, feel, and think only what Andi is seeing, hearing, feeling, or thinking. She doesn't see her brother sneaking up behind her to rescue her, so the reader shouldn't see him, either.

Now read the same scene from the older brother's point of view:

#2-   Chad rounded the corner of the barn and stopped short. To his horror, his youngest sister sat boldly atop the corral fence, her hand outstretched for that monster horse to take a bite. He opened his mouth to shout a warning then quickly clamped his jaw shut. There was no telling how the stallion would react to the noise.

Slowly, so as not to startle the horse, he crept closer and closer to the pair. Then, without warning, the stallion reared up. Chad leaped for Andi, grasped the back of her overalls, and gave her a toss. She tumbled to the ground a safe distance from the corral.

Chad stood over her, breathing hard. His fear exploded into outrage when he saw her safe and sound. "What were you doing?" he bellowed. "You could have been killed!"

Point of View Bloopers

Did you notice the difference points of view in the two scenes?

Read the scene below and decide who the point-of-view character is. The viewpoint character is: _____

    Jon crouched behind a stump, breathing hard. His heart pounded. Sweat trickled down the back of his neck. *What if he sees me?* he wondered. *He'll kill me for sure!* Just then a twig snapped. Jon leaped to his feet and raced for a new hiding place. *How will I ever escape?* He'd never been so scared.

    Sarah called and called, but Jon didn't answer. Disgusted, she scowled and slammed the door shut. "Mom, Jon's disappeared again. He's always running off."

    Mom felt bad. She wished Jon would stick around home. It always frightened her when her son wandered off to the woods. Strange things happened in that forest. *What if he doesn't come home?* she asked herself.

Was it hard to decide who the viewpoint character is? The author begins the scene from Jon's point of view, but then changes points of view two more times—to Sarah and to Mom. Underline the clues in the above scene that show you the author has changed points of view.

    Jon crouched behind a stump, breathing hard. His heart pounded. Sweat trickled down the back of his neck. *What if he sees me?* he wondered. *He'll kill me for sure!* Just then a twig snapped. Jon leaped to his feet and raced for a new hiding place. *How will I ever escape?* He'd never been so scared.

    Sarah called and called, but Jon didn't answer. <u>Disgusted, she scowled</u> and slammed the door shut. "Mom, Jon's disappeared again. He's always running off." [**the reader also knows that Sarah is not in the woods with Jon. The setting has changed.**]

    <u>Mom felt bad. She wished Jon would stick around home. It always frightened her when her son wandered off to the woods.</u> Strange things happened in that forest. *<u>What if he doesn't come home?</u> <u>she asked herself.</u>* [**Another character's thoughts are a sure giveaway that the point of view has changed.**]

Chapter and Scene Breaks

Sometimes you have two main characters that are equally important to the story. For example, a brother-and-sister detective team, or two best friends on a treasure hunt. Maybe you really want to tell your story from both characters' viewpoints. It's possible to do it, but *never* switch character viewpoints in the same scene.

You can use two different tricks to alert the reader to a change in viewpoint:

1) Start a new chapter from the new character's viewpoint
2) Use a scene break

    Jon crouched behind a stump, breathing hard. His heart pounded. Sweat trickled down the back of his neck. *What if he sees me?* he wondered. *He'll kill me for sure!* Just then a twig snapped. Jon leaped to his feet and raced for a new hiding place. *How will I ever escape?* He'd never been so scared.

* * * [scene break]

    Sarah called and called, but Jon didn't answer. She slammed the door shut. "Mom, Jon's disappeared again. He's always running off."
    <u>She knew</u> her mom felt bad. <u>Sarah</u> wished Jon would stick around home. It always frightened her when <u>her brother</u> wandered off to the woods. Strange things happened in that forest. *What if he doesn't come home?* <u>Sarah</u> asked herself.

With a few minor changes, this story now jumps from Jon's POV (point of view) to Sarah's. The scene break lets the reader know there is a new setting and a new character. It reads much smoother this way.

```
****************************************************************
*                        Writer's Hint                        *
*                                                             *
*   Use words like: obviously, apparently, looked like, she knew,  *
*     it seemed, and clearly to keep your point of view consistent. *
*                                                             *
****************************************************************
```

It's Your Turn

Choose a scene from a favorite book (or movie) and rewrite the scene from a different character's point of view. For example:

1) If your favorite book is a *Little House* book, you could rewrite a scene from Nellie Oleson's point of view. What would Nellie see or feel as she's dancing by the creek with leeches attached to her legs?

2) Or . . . rewrite a scene from *The Lion, the Witch, and the Wardrobe* from Aslan's point of view. What would he be thinking or feeling while the White Witch is having him bound and shaved and humiliated? Use your imagination!

3) Or . . . write a scene from an unusual point of view. For example, write a scene from the viewpoint of a gold nugget lying in the river. A giant hand snatches you from your home! What happens to you (the gold nugget)? How do you feel?

4) Or . . . take a scene from the story you are creating and rewrite it from one of your other character's points of view (like the dog's!)

Practice this on more than one scene from your favorite books or movies.

Point of View

_____

_____

_____

_____

_____

_____

_____

_____

_____

_____

_____

_____

_____

_____

_____

_____

_____

_____

_____

_____

_____

_____

_____

Point of View

_____

_____

_____

_____

_____

_____

_____

_____

_____

_____

_____

_____

_____

_____

_____

_____

_____

_____

_____

_____

Point of View

_____

_____

_____

_____

_____

_____

_____

_____

_____

_____

_____

_____

_____

_____

_____

_____

_____

_____

_____

_____

Ups & Downs

Give readers a ride they'll remember;
Keep them guessing what's 'round the next bend.
Make your character seem like he won't reach his dream,
Then let him succeed in the end!

Okay. You've hooked your readers with a great beginning. They love your lead character. You've taken "snapshots" to make readers feel they can see the setting as you tell the story. Your scenes have action, dialogue, description, and more! Now what?

When you put your scenes together, do it in such a way that your character has "ups and downs" in his journey to solve his problem. Think of it as a roller coaster ride. Your character wants something, but you can't let him have it. Something bad happens to prevent it. He drops "down." As he goes along, good things happen, making the character think he is on the road to reaching his goal. These are the high points of the story, the "ups."

After an "up" there is usually another "down," just like on a roller coaster. Eventually your character reaches his worst "down," also known as his "darkest moment." The reader doesn't know if your character will survive or make the wrong choice. This is known as the **CLIMAX**.

Following the climax, you need to tie up any loose ends and quickly bring the story to a **RESOLUTION**, using the elements of a satisfying ending.

****
Writer's Hint

Another word for the "ups and downs" in a story is: **CONFLICT**
****

Ups & Downs

Let's determine the ups and downs for our lead character, Jack, in the story, "Jack and the Beanstalk." First of all, let's summarize the plot.

> **"Nutshell" summary:** In an effort to keep himself and his widowed mother from starving, Jack embarks on a journey to regain the family treasure, which lies in the possession of a cruel and dangerous giant.

HOOK: We meet Jack, and quickly learn he is a likeable fellow. He is also careless and lazy. Right away we learn this family has a **PROBLEM**—they are very poor and in danger of starving to death.

DOWN: There is no more food in the house.

UP: They do have a cow, which Jack is instructed to sell.

DOWN: Jack trades the cow for some brightly colored beans. Now things are worse. Mother tosses the beans out the window in despair.

UP: The beans sprout overnight and reach to the sky. Jack climbs the beanstalk and discovers a beautiful castle in the clouds.

DOWN: Jack meets a fairy and learns that the castle once belonged to his father, whom the giant killed.

UP: Jack is told how he can get his family's riches back.

DOWN: Jack gets caught by the giant's wife.

UP: She hides Jack from the giant so he can work for her. Later, he steals the hen that lays golden eggs, returns home, and presents the gift to his mother. (The story could end here, but it doesn't).

DOWN: Jack becomes restless and decides to climb the beanstalk again.

UP: The giant's wife hires him to work for her.

DOWN (leading to the climax): When Jack steals a harp, it shouts for the giant. (Things will get worse from now on.)

CLIMAX: The giant chases Jack and follows him down the beanstalk. Jack grabs an ax and chops down the beanstalk. The giant crashes and dies.

RESOLUTION: The fairy appears and tells Jack he has acted bravely and has won back the family treasure. The castle returns to earth.

ENDING (typical fairy tale ending): Jack and his mother live happily ever after.

It's Your Turn

Think of a favorite book or movie. Write a nutshell summary. Now, try to identify the hook, the problem, and the ups and downs of the story You may not need to use all the lines. Practice makes perfect!

"Nutshell" summary: _____

_____

_____

Hook: _____

Problem (first "down"): _____

_____

_____

Up: _____

Down: _____

Up: _____

Down: _____

Up: _____

Down: _____

CLIMAX (darkest moment): _____

_____

_____

_____

Resolution: _____

_____

Satisfying Ending: _____

_____

_____

 Your Story

Title of your story: _____

Nutshell Summary: _____

_____

Hook: _____

Problem (first "down"): _____

_____

_____

Up: _____

Down: _____

Up: _____

Down: _____

Up: _____

Down: _____

Up: _____

Down: _____

CLIMAX (darkest moment): _____

_____

_____

_____

Resolution: _____

_____

Satisfying Ending: _____

_____

Another Story

Title of your story: _____

Nutshell Summary: _____

_____

Hook: _____

Problem (first "down"): _____

_____

_____

Up: _____

Down: _____

Up: _____

Down: _____

Up: _____

Down: _____

Up: _____

Down: _____

CLIMAX (darkest moment): _____

_____

_____

_____

Resolution: _____

_____

Satisfying Ending: _____

_____

Another Story

Title of your story: _____

Nutshell Summary: _____

_____

Hook: _____

Problem (first "down"): _____

_____

_____

Up: _____

Down: _____

Up: _____

Down: _____

Up: _____

Down: _____

Up: _____

Down: _____

CLIMAX (darkest moment): _____

_____

_____

_____

Resolution: _____

_____

Satisfying Ending: _____

_____

The Ending

The ending is important—
Like the frosting on a cake.
If you make it satisfying, your readers will keep crying
For other thrilling stories you create.

How do you feel when you come to the end of a good book? Happy? Satisfied? Content? What if the book ended with, "...and that's the end of the story." Wouldn't you feel cheated? You bet you would! A satisfying ending (even if it's sad) makes the reader want to go back and read the book again—and again.

****
Writer's Hint

To keep your "fish" on the line, remember that the middle of the story—and especially the ENDING—is just as important as the beginning hook.
****

Were you able to give your story a satisfying ending on the previous pages (the Ups and Downs)? If not, this "Ending" lesson is for you.

You can create a "good" ending to your stories by putting one or more of these elements into your endings.

****
Writer's Hint

Memorize these Ending Elements:

A MEMORY of what the character has been through.
The main character's **FEELINGS** about his adventure.
What the main character **HOPES** for the future.
A reminder of a **DECISION** the main character has made as a result of solving the story problem.
****

Good Story Endings

Sometimes it helps if you can see examples of how authors ended their stories in a way that makes you want to read the book again. For each of the story endings below, underline in different colors the ENDING ELEMENTS the author used (most did not use them all).

A MEMORY: red
FEELINGS: blue
HOPES or DREAMS for the future: green
A DECISION: brown

Charlotte's Web by E.B. White: Wilbur never forgot Charlotte. Although he loved her children and grandchildren dearly, none of the new spiders ever quite took her place in his heart. She was in a class by herself. It is not often that someone comes along who is a true friend and a good writer. Charlotte was both.

Ralph. S. Mouse by Beverly Cleary: Ralph remained behind at the inn, where he rides around every night in his sports car, generously giving rides to his relatives and enjoying their company now that they have bene-fited from his education. He is strict about one thing, however. Ralph is the only mouse who sits in the driver's seat of the Laser XL7.

Caddie Woodlawn by Carol Ryrie Brink: "What a lot has happened since last year when I dropped the nuts all over the dining room floor. How far I've come! I'm the same girl and yet not the same. I wonder if it's always like that? Folks keep growing from one person into another all their lives, and life is just a lot of everyday adventures. Well, whatever it is, I like it." The late afternoon sun flooded her face with golden light. Looking toward the approaching rider, her face was turned to the west. It was always to be turned westward now, for Caddie Woodlawn was a pioneer and an American.

The Last Battle by C.S. Lewis: All their life in this world and all their adventures in Narnia had only been the cover and the title page: now at last they were beginning Chapter One of the Great Story which no one on earth has read: which goes on forever: in which every chapter is better than the one before.

Andrea Carter and the San Francisco Smugglers by Susan K. Marlow:

Andi looked around the table. She wanted to go home to the ranch and Taffy, but how could she say good-bye to her new friends now? She heard the shrill laughter of Levi and Betsy from the room next door and realized she hadn't spent much time with her nieces and nephew either. And of course she wanted to be in the city when Justin came back for the hearing for Lin Mei and Kum Ju.

She took a deep breath and said, "I'll stay."

The Missing Link: Found by Christina and Felice Gerwitz:

David looked up and smiled in amazement. "Life sure isn't boring with you guys around. I think we need to visit more often."

A look of agreement crossed everyone's faces. They looked forward to spending time together.

"So, Uncle Mike," Christian ventured, "when's the next excavation scheduled for?"

Dr. Murphy and Anna shook their heads and laughed. "No more digging!"

Little Britches by Ralph Moody: Father had always said grace before meals; always the same twenty-five words, and the ritual was always the same. Mother would look around the table to see that everything was in readiness; then she would nod to Father. That night she nodded to me, and I became a man.

How NOT to End Your Story

Most published authors write pretty good endings to their stories. If they didn't, they probably wouldn't be published. Many beginning writers, however—especially young writers—come to the end of their story and just stop. Here are some ways NOT to end your story:

~And that is the end of my story.
~After we left the river, we went home and went to bed.
~They lived happily ever after (unless you're writing a fairy tale).
~I never went to Joe's house again.

Okay. I admit it. These are pretty simple examples. But even if you are an older and more advanced writer, your endings might fall flat if you don't put as much thought into them as you do when you create a great beginning hook.

****
Writer's Hint

A technique that works well to end your story is to come "full circle" and remind readers of something the character struggled with in the beginning of the story that he or she has now overcome.
****

Example: In *Andrea Carter and the San Francisco Smugglers*, my main character, Andi, does not want to go to school in the city, far away from her ranch home. To bring it "full circle" I ended the book with her decision to stay in the city and complete the school term. This ties the two events together and shows the character's growth.

It's Your Turn

You are going to revise some boring story endings—without reading the whole story. That will be challenging, but you can make up some of the story details. You might need to create a memory or two. Give it a try!

<u>Boring Ending</u>: I won the race, and that is the end of my story.

Four Ending Elements

<u>Memory:</u> Tape breaking; crossing the finish line; the crowd cheering
<u>Feeling</u> (excited): Heart pounds; leaps in the air
<u>Hope:</u> plans for next race.
<u>Decision:</u> Run every day to keep in shape

Good Ending

I'll never forget the tape breaking across my chest as I crossed the finish line. My heart pounded when I heard the crowd cheering my victory. I hope I do as well at my next track meet. I know I'll be running every day and working extra hard to keep in shape!

Examples

Here are some student samples of good story endings.

<u>Before</u> (boring ending): And that is the story of how I saved my little sister from drowning.

<u>Memory:</u> sister's shriek, horror felt at sound of splash

<u>Feeling:</u> shivering, realizing how much I love her

<u>Hope:</u> we wouldn't fight

<u>Decision:</u> to always remember that day

<u>Revised ending:</u> I stretched and soaked in the warmth of my bed. Shuddering, I recalled Mary's shriek as she slipped through the rails and the horror I felt come over me when I heard the splash that her body made when it hit the water. I knew then that I loved her more then anything else in the world. I hoped that this would keep us from fighting with each other. I resolved right then and there that whenever I was tempted to get mad at her I would remember that fateful day.   ~ Lulu

* * *

<u>Before</u> (boring ending): Just as the space creature opened its mouth to eat me, I woke up. It was only a dream.

<u>A memory:</u> the monster's yellow eyes

<u>A feeling:</u> pounding heart

<u>A hope:</u> to never see the creature again

<u>A decision:</u> to never watch scary movies and eat sugar before bed again

<u>Revised ending:</u> Just as the space creature opened its mouth to eat me, I woke up. Relief seeped through me as I tried to slow down my racing heart. The creature's yellow eyes flashed back into my mind and I shook my head to disperse the remembrance. It was gone. It had been a dream. I'd never see it again. Yes, there was no more need to worry. I laid my head on my pillow and determined never again to eat sugary food and watch creepy movies before bed.   ~Amber

It's Your Turn

Turn these boring endings into satisfying endings. You don't have to use EVERY element. Pick and choose the ones you like.

Before: After my big climbing adventure, I went home and went to bed.

A memory? _____

A feeling? _____

A hope? _____

A decision? _____

Revised Ending: _____

_____

_____

_____

_____

_____

_____

_____

_____

_____

_____

_____

_____

_____

_____

One More Time!

Or make up your own ending if you don't like the examples I've used.

Before: And that's what happened after the wild horse trampled me.

A memory? _____

A feeling? _____

A hope? _____

A decision? _____

Revised Ending: _____

_____

_____

_____

_____

_____

_____

_____

_____

_____

_____

_____

_____

_____

_____

My Story Ending

Have you thought about how *your* story might end? Here is a page to
write some notes and jot down some possible endings to your story.

A memory? _____

A feeling? _____

A hope? _____

A decision? _____

Ending: _____

_____

_____

_____

_____

_____

_____

_____

_____

_____

_____

_____

_____

_____

_____

_____

_____

Revising Your Story

Just when you think you are finished,
And your story has come to an end,
Pick it up and go back, revising's a snap!
Then your book will be ready to send.

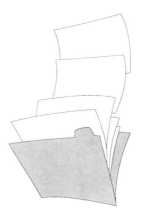

At last! Your story is finished. You've hooked your reader. The ups and downs have carried him or her on a journey that finished with a satisfying ending. Your writing camera has done its job, providing vivid details. Story glue holds your plot together. You're done. Breathe a sigh of relief.

Now, take a deep breath and get ready for the *real* work! What you have created is the rough draft. Your ideas have flowed onto paper and the story's good. Very good. Now the time has come to roll up your sleeves, sharpen your pencil or turn on your computer, and begin the editing process.

   It's time to get the "bugs" out of your story!

These next several pages introduce you to some of the common mistakes beginning writers make. Everybody is a beginner at one time or another. The lessons here will take you to the next level in your writing journey.

If you ever decide to submit (send) your story to a publisher, you want to make your story the best it can be. Learning to self-edit your own work puts you at the head of the pack.

Verb Tense

It's time for a review of "verbs." You've used them in your story, but perhaps you don't know what they are. The verb is the key word of the sentence. It shows action or a state of being. Without a verb, you have no sentence.

The other word you need to know is "tense." It does not mean you are stressed out. In this case, "verb tense" means how you tell your story. The common choices are: PRESENT TENSE or PAST TENSE. Confused? Here are some examples:

<u>Present</u>: run, jump, is, see, hear, stamp, call, laugh, cry, fight,

<u>Past</u>: ran, jumped, was, saw, stamped, called, laughed, cried, fought,

Nutshell summaries are written in the present tense. Stories are usually written in the past tense. This may sound simple. However, the "bug" you need to remove from your writing is when you mix up the present tense and the past tense in the same story.

All of the main verbs in this scene have been underlined.

"Come on," Tyler <u>called</u> to the group standing on shore. "Get in. Let's go!"

Josh <u>pauses</u> and <u>looks</u> around. He <u>is</u> not sure he <u>wants</u> to step into that leaky old raft.

Rachel <u>jumped</u> in and <u>reached</u> out a hand. "Hurry, Josh."

"I think this is a bad idea," Josh <u>said</u>, stepping into the raft. He <u>is</u> not at all happy, especially when he <u>hears</u> the sound of the rapids close by. "Are you sure it's safe?"

"Of course it is," Tyler <u>said</u>. "What's the problem?"

Circle the PAST TENSE verbs. Put a box around the PRESENT TENSE verbs.

Past Or Present?

How did you do? Could you tell the difference?

"Come on," Tyler (called) to the group standing on shore. "Get in. Let's go!"

Josh [pauses] and [looks] around. He [is] not sure he [wants] to step into that leaky old raft.

Rachel (jumped) in and (reached) out a hand. "Hurry, Josh."

"I think this is a bad idea," Josh (said) stepping into the raft. He [is] not at all happy, especially when he [hears] the sound of the rapids close by. "Are you sure it's safe?"

"Of course it is," Tyler (said) "What's the problem?"

★ ★ ★

The last step is to change the verbs in the boxes to past tense verbs, in order to keep the story consistent.

★ ★ ★

"Come on," Tyler <u>called</u> to the group standing on shore. "Get in."

Josh _____ and _____ around. He _____ not sure he _____ to step into that leaky old raft.

Rachel <u>jumped</u> in and <u>reached</u> out a hand. "Hurry, Josh."

"I think this is a bad idea," Josh <u>said</u>, stepping into the raft. He

_____ not at all happy, especially when he _____ the sound of the rapids close by. "Are you sure it's safe?"

"Of course it is!" Tyler <u>said</u>. "What's the problem?"

It's Your Turn

The paragraph below is a mess! The important "story-telling" verbs have been underlined. Some of them are correct—in past tense—but some are in present tense. The second paragraph contains blanks. Fill in the blanks with the correct verb tense to keep this scene in the past tense. (some do not need to be changed)

Hamid <u>rolled</u> off his mattress, <u>washed</u> his face and hands in a bucket, and <u>started</u> to eat his breakfast. Gobbling his bread and sipping his bowl of coffee, he <u>glances</u> at his mother. Her face <u>is</u> pale, and there <u>are</u> dark circles under her eyes, but she <u>does</u> not look as unhappy as he <u>had expected</u>. There <u>is</u> a very determined expression in her face, as though she <u>has</u> quite made up her mind about something. Once, Hamid <u>found</u> her staring hard at him, and he <u>returned</u> her gaze, steady and equally determined. She <u>raises</u> her eyebrows a little and he <u>gives</u> a slight nod. A secret understanding <u>flashes</u> between them. At the earliest possible opportunity they <u>would hold</u> council together.

Hamid _____ off his mattress, _____ his face and hands in a bucket, and _____ to eat his breakfast. Gobbling his bread and sipping his bowl of coffee, he _____ at his mother. Her face _____ pale, and there _____ dark circles under her eyes, but she _____ not look as unhappy as he _____ _____. There _____ a very determined expression in her face, as though she had quite made up her mind about something. Once, Hamid _____ her staring hard at him, and he _____ her gaze, steady and equally determined. She _____ her eyebrows a little and he _____ a slight nod. A secret understanding _____ between them. At the earliest possible opportunity they _____ _____ council together.

~ from *Star of Light* by Patricia M. St. John

Person (first, second, third)

Another "bug" that creeps into your writing is the idea of "person." When you write your story, you have three choices:

First person: "I" "me" "we" "us" The character is telling the story from his or her own point of view (POV).

Second person: "you" The author is talking to the reader (this is hardly ever used).

Third person: "he" "she" "they" "them" This is very common. The character is telling the story, but not using "I."

When you write your story, feel free to use either first person or third person, but don't use both in the same story!

For example:

Darkness swallowed the explorers as they trudged through the shallow snow that blew into the ancient cave. Far off in the cave they heard two voices that belonged to robbers that wanted the treasure. We sneaked past the robbers and crawled through a tunnel that was four feet high by seven feet wide.

"Hey!" shouted my companion, "I think I just hit something!" Sure enough, there was a red and gold chest right in front of our faces. The chest had three latches and some vertical silver lines that were an inch thick. There were nails every three inches and a head of a dragon engraved in the front.   ~Brandon

This is a great little scene, but the writer switched from third person (the explorers) to first person (we) partway through the story. This switching confuses the reader.

Keep this bug out of your story!

It's Your Turn

This scene, from Jody's POV, should be written in 3rd person. Circle the words that shows the author switched to 1st person.

Jody laid his new fishing pole over his shoulder and scurried to catch up to his older brothers. We had already climbed into our family's prized possession--a green and black inflatable boat that had only one slow leak.

"Hurry up, Jody!" Michael yelled, tossing the bait box into the raft. "The fish won't be biting much longer."

Jody tripped and sprawled in the bottom of the boat. His pole went flying. *Great,* he thought, *My very first fishing trip, and I'm a klutz.* Michael yanked me by the seat of my pants and pulled me the rest of the way into the boat.

Tyler began rowing. The sun shone down, hot and bright. The lake was as smooth as glass as we baited our hooks and threw the lines in. Jody watched carefully. He bit his lip, squeezed his eyes shut, and smeared the power bait onto his hook.

"This stuff's gross," I said. No one answered. Michael and Tyler were sprawled out in the raft, clearly enjoying the quiet afternoon.

Plop! Jody threw his line overboard. He sighed, happy to have baited his hook successfully. I held tightly to my pole, waiting for the giant fish to snatch up the bait.

Nothing. Jody slumped. I listened to the *swish, swish* of water lapping against the rubber boat and yawned. My brothers began to tell stories of past fishing trips.

Suddenly Jody's pole jerked from his hands. Just in time, he caught the end. "Help!" I shouted. The boat rocked as Michael and Tyler sat straight up.

"Reel him in, Jody!" Tyler screamed.

"I betcha he's twenty inches," Michael added.

Jody held onto his pole for dear life and reeled in the line. *It won't reel in! The fish is pulling too hard!* he thought.

"Want me to take over?" Michael asked.

"No!" Jody said between clenched teeth. "This is *my* fish."

The fish suddenly jumped out of the water. All of us gasped. It was the largest trout we had ever seen. Shining silver and pink and black, it flipped and plunged back into the lake.

Tyler whistled. "Little brother, that's some fish. Reel it in!"

Did You Find Them?

I underlined the words that showed the author switched from 3rd person to 1st person in this scene. Did you find them all?

Jody laid his new fishing pole over his shoulder and scurried to catch up to his older brothers. **We** had already climbed into **our** family's prized possession--a green and black inflatable boat that had only one slow leak.

"Hurry up, Jody!" Michael yelled, tossing the bait box into the raft. "The fish won't be biting much longer."

Jody tripped and sprawled in the bottom of the boat. His pole went flying. *Great,* he thought, *My very first fishing trip, and I'm a klutz.* Michael yanked **me** by the seat of **my** pants and pulled **me** the rest of the way into the boat.

Tyler began rowing. The sun shone down, hot and bright. The lake was as smooth as glass as **we** baited our hooks and threw the lines in. Jody watched carefully. He bit his lip, squeezed his eyes shut, and smeared the power bait onto his hook.

"This stuff's gross," **I** said. No one answered. Michael and Tyler were sprawled out in the raft, clearly enjoying the quiet afternoon.

Plop! Jody threw his line overboard. He sighed, happy to have baited his hook successfully. **I** held tightly to my pole, waiting for the giant fish to snatch up the bait.

Nothing. Jody slumped. **I** listened to the *swish, swish* of water lapping against the rubber boat and yawned. **My** brothers began to tell stories of past fishing trips.

Suddenly Jody's pole jerked from his hands. Just in time, he caught the end. "Help!" **I** shouted. The boat rocked as Michael and Tyler sat straight up.

"Reel him in, Jody!" Tyler screamed.

"I betcha he's twenty inches," Michael added.

Jody held onto his pole for dear life and reeled in the line. *It won't reel in! The fish is pulling too hard!* he thought.

"Want me to take over?" Michael asked.

"No!" Jody said between clenched teeth. "This is *my* fish."

The fish suddenly jumped out of the water. **All of us** gasped. It was the largest trout **we** had ever seen. Shining silver and pink and black, it flipped and plunged back into the lake.

Tyler whistled. "Little brother, that's some fish. Reel it in!"

Pest Words

If you read your story out loud, you will soon discover some words that you like to use over and over. My favorite word was "just." I didn't realize I used it so much! Here are words that are overused. Notice how I changed the sentences to get rid of the "bugs."

1) <u>Just</u>- Once or twice is OK, but don't use too many.

2) <u>That</u>- I thought <u>that</u> I knew the answer, but I didn't. **I thought I knew the answer, but I didn't.**

3) <u>There was</u>- <u>There was</u> a horse standing in my front yard! **A horse stood in my front yard!**

4) <u>Would</u>- Mom <u>would</u> fix supper and then we <u>would</u> eat. **Mom fixed supper and then we ate.**

5) <u>It was, that was</u>- <u>It was</u> morning and I was doing my schoolwork. <u>That was</u> when I heard the doorbell ring. **One morning when I was doing my schoolwork, I heard the doorbell ring.**

6) <u>But</u>- Do not begin sentences with this word. "It is my toy and I don't have to share." But when Mom heard this, she scolded Jon. **"It is my toy and I don't have to share." When Mom heard this, she scolded Jon.**

7) <u>About</u>- Sarah reminded Timmy <u>about</u> what their mom told them. **Sarah reminded Timmy what their mom told them.**

8) <u>Then</u>- Peter took the dogs outside. Then he saw someone running. **Peter took the dogs outside. He saw someone running.**

More Bugs!

Two more big "bugs" can infest your writing.

1) Adverbs are words that tell more about verbs. Many end in "-ly": Happi**ly**, careful**ly**, sad**ly**, perfect**ly**, wonderful**ly**, terri**bly**. These turn into pest words when used too often. They are lazy words. Choose "strong" verbs instead.

Examples:

~ Mary <u>held</u> the railing <u>tightly</u>. Change to: Mary <u>gripped</u> the railing.

~ Jon <u>talked loudly</u>. Change to: Jon <u>shouted</u>.

~ The deer <u>ran</u> away <u>quickly</u>. Change to: The deer <u>bounded</u> away.

2) "-ing" words are verbs that become pests when used over and over. They are especially bad bugs when used with dialogue tags (remember those?).

Examples:

~ "I love it!" Anna yelled, <u>hanging</u> over the railing.

~ <u>Smiling</u>, Suzy said, "Don't forget me."

~ "That's awesome!" Joey agreed, <u>staring</u> at the new car.

~ <u>Hunkering</u> down, Chris tried to reach the hammer.

~ <u>Squinting</u>, Peter looked into the noon sky.

Or worse! Double-bug infestations! Using "-ing" and "-ly" words together:

~ Tyler raced for his bike, <u>hastily tossing</u> the rock aside

~ <u>Smiling sheepishly</u>, Mary <u>quickly</u> slid over.

~ "Hurry, Dad!" Paul shouted, <u>trying hopelessly</u> to hang on to the ledge.

~ "We won!" Tom said <u>excitedly</u>, <u>echoing</u> his brother's shout of victory.

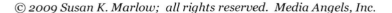

It's Your Turn

Go through your story and get rid of the bugs—those pest words that infest your writing and make it drag. As astonishing as this may sound, there are published books out there, written by adults, that are infested with many of these pest words. Below is a box for your bugs. As you revise your story, see how many words you can identify as your favorite words, or especially the *big* bugs—"-ing" and "-ly" words.

Remember: it's OK to use these words occasionally. It's only when they get out of control that you have a pest problem.

_____

_____

_____

_____

_____

_____

_____

_____

_____

_____

_____

_____

_____

_____

_____

_____

_____

What Now?

You've learned about summaries and settings,
Beginnings and endings and plot;
You've learned point of view, so what's left for you?
Just one simple question: "Now what?"

You've come to the end of the *Reach for the Stars* writing workbook, but your writing journey has just begun. Maybe you filled out every lesson, and all the blank story pages as well. Or perhaps you're still trying to figure out how everything fits together. Either way, you can use what you've learned to write more (and better) stories.

If you are wondering "What now?" here are some opportunities:

1) Become a member of the Reach for the Stars Writing club. It's free! You'll receive e-zines with games and writing ideas, as well as being the first to know when we're having a story-writing contest (with great prizes). You won't want to miss out! Sign up at the Reach for the Stars blog at www.reach-for-the-stars-workshop.blogspot.com or at www.mediaangels.com/reachforthestars

2) There are many other contests out there for young writers. For a list of web links to contests, go to the Reach for the Stars blog.

3) If you have questions or comments for Mrs. Marlow, you can e-mail her at susankmarlow@mediaangels.com. Share your favorite lesson or a nutshell summary from a story you want to write. She'd love to hear from you!

Keep reaching for the stars!

Story Pages

For Parents and Teachers

These pages offer suggestions on how to teach the lessons: ideas for making a concept come alive, activities to reinforce a new writing skill, or just hints to have fun!

PAGES 13-22: Begin the habit of reading books with "Author Eyes." Ask which genre the books they're reading belong in. See if you can identify the 5 elements in books and in movies. The deeper you dig into a book to learn how the author put it together, the better writers your young readers will become. Ask questions like: "What did the author do to grab your interest right from the start?" "How was the author able to make you laugh during a scene?" "What did he do to let you 'see' an object?"

PAGES 23-36 CHARACTERS: Involve students in a discussion about their favorite books/movies/real life characters. Focus on what personality traits draw them to a particular character. If interest is high, discuss characters they don't like/fear. • Choosing names for characters is fun! Check out baby name books from the library or go on-line. Give children time to ponder and see if they can get a mental picture of their characters from the names alone. Remind them they are choosing names for possible characters in a story they may later want to write. Most kids like to share names when asked, and they are excited to be creating a brand-new person—even a pretend one. • Let the children read over the character traits chart and start filling in their character charts. • Underscore the idea that a person's "inside" characteristics are more important than the outward, physical characteristics. Have volunteers read his/her character's physical and personality traits/dislikes, then guide the children into turning these notes into complete sentences as a Character Sketch. The skill here is turning notes into a complete paragraph.

PAGES 37-49 SHOW-DON'T-TELL: Ask kids "What do feelings look like?" Allow discussion, then show kids the model sentence on page 37. Have a volunteer act out what Paul looks like when he is angry. Have the volunteer "freeze" and ask for words that describe what they see in Paul. Explain that while we can see feelings easily on a movie screen, writers must make readers "see" by using words that make a picture in the reader's head. You can do this with as many feelings as you have time for. They all want to get up and show a feeling!

FEELING ACTIVITY CARDS: Cut out the Feelings cards and follow the instructions. This activity works great with groups of 3 or 4. The groups take turns sharing in front of the class. The rest of the students try to guess which feeling the group is describing in words. Discuss other words that could describe that feeling. They'll do this activity as many times as you let them!

PAGES 50-67 SETTING AND DESCRIPTION: Bring a camera and talk about "writing cameras" and "word pictures." Find a picture of a castle, a ship, a comical puppy, or something unusual and use only general words to describe it (don't show the kids). Have kids draw what you've described. When you show them your picture, have a discussion of why some words don't do a good job of describing. You can play this game any number of times. • Play the Dead Word game: say a word (like "yellow") and ask if it is a dead word and why or why not. Once the kids get the hang of it, they can offer words or phrases. Encourage kids to add dead words to their Dead Word jail. • Find vivid descriptions from good kids' literature and read them aloud. • Write a "telling" sentence and have the group help you change it to a showing sentence. • Write "telling" sentences on the backs of photographs of animals, unusual buildings, space battles, other children—anything that would make a good subject for a "writing camera." Distribute the photographs and ask students to change the boring sentence into a word picture using their "writing cameras." This activity leads into the practice pages.

PAGES 69-81 BEGINNING HOOKS: Bring a fishing pole and bait (both good and useless). Discuss fishing and what attracts a fish to the line. Make the transfer from fishing for fish to an author fishing for a reader and drawing him in by baiting his hook with good openings. • Read openings from a variety of books—good beginnings and boring beginnings. Discuss why the opening made you want to continue reading or why it didn't. After introducing the seven techniques an author can use, see if the kids can determine which "bait" (or baits) the author used.

PAGES 82-91 NUTSHELLS & DIALOGUE: Create paper "nuts" that open, with lined paper inside the "nuts," for kids to write 1-2 sentence summaries of books and movies. • Copy excerpts from children's literature onto overheads (or run off copies for all students), with the dialogue strung together. Discuss with the group how to fix it. Highlight the different speakers in the dialogue.

PAGES 92-112 SCENES, POV, and UPS & DOWNS: Find a short scene from a DVD (I use Anne and Diana chasing the cow out of Mrs. Lynde's cabbage patch, *Anne of Avonlea*). Discuss the elements of a visual scene and how to create a scene with words. • Have kids write a scene from an unusual point of view, like from a gold nugget's. Or rewrite a scene from a favorite book from a different character's POV (like the black Stallion instead of Alec). Or of a volcano as it's erupting. Think outside the box. • After going over Jack and the Beanstalk, discuss the ups and downs of other familiar stories.

PAGES 113-121 THE ENDING: Copy the endings of good books on overheads or a white board. Use different colors to highlight as students identify the elements authors included in their satisfying endings. • Have kids write new endings to their favorite

About the Author

Susan K. Marlow started writing stories when she was ten years old, but she wrote them only for herself. It wasn't until years later, with the publication of her first book, *Andrea Carter and the Long Ride Home*, that Susan discovered it's more fun to share her stories than to keep them to herself. (If you want to read some of Susan's childhood stories, go to www.susankmarlow.com for the link.)

Susan has a BA degree in elementary education from Washington State University and more than twenty years teaching experience in private and homeschooling fields. She is the author of the Circle C Adventures series for 'tweens from Kregel Publications. In addition to writing, Susan speaks at Young Author conferences, teaches writing workshops for kids, and serves as a freelance editor. She and her family make their home in Washington State.

HORSES, ADVENTURE, AND THE OLD WEST!

Circle C Adventures series

Book 1: *Andrea Carter and the Long Ride Home*

Andi's poor choices plunge her into danger when she takes her horse, Taffy, and leaves her home on the Circle C Ranch. Set in 1880s California.

Book 2: *Andrea Carter and the Dangerous Decision*

Andi's frightening experiences with an outlaw captor result in a new understanding of what the Golden Rule really means.

Book 3: *Andrea Carter and the Family Secret*

Andi's carefree life on the Circle C ranch is shattered by the arrival of strangers who hold the key to a shocking family secret from the past.

Book4: *Andrea Carter and the San Francisco Smugglers*

Andi takes charge when she learns that the little Chinese servant girl at her San Francisco boarding school is really a slave.

Book 5: *Andrea Carter and the Trouble with Treasure*

Andi's dreams of treasure turn into a life-or-death struggle when she and her friends seek gold in the Sierra Nevada range.

Book 6: *Andrea Carter and the Price of Truth*

Andi's eyewitness testimony places a beloved citizen of Fresno at the scene of a crime. Will the price of truth be too high if it means losing Taffy forever?

Resources

Mariconda, Barbara. *The Most Wonderful Writing Lessons Ever*. Jefferson City, MO: Scholastic Professional Books, 1999.

Reece, Colleen. *Writing Smarter not Harder*. Edgewood, WA: Kaleidoscope Press, 1995.

Excerpts

Brink, Carol Ryrie. *Caddie Woodlawn*. New York, NY. Aladdin, 1997.

Cleary, Beverly. *Ralph S. Mouse*. New York, NY. HarperCollins, 1993.

Gerwitz, Christina and Felice. *The Missing Link: Found*. Fort Meyer, FL. Media Angels, Inc., 2004.

Kehret, Peg. *Night of Fear*. New York, NY. Aladdin, 1996.

Key, Alexander. *The Forgotten Door*. New York, NY. Scholastic Inc., 1965.

Lewis, C.S. *The Last Battle*. New York, NY. HarperCollins, 1984.

Marlow, Susan K. *Andrea Carter and the Family Secret*. Grand Rapids, MI, Kregel Publications, 2008.

Marlow, Susan K. *Andrea Carter and the Long Ride Home*. Grand Rapids, MI, Kregel Publications, 2005.

Marlow, Susan K. *Andrea Carter and the San Francisco Smugglers*. Grand Rapids, MI, Kregel Publications, 2008.

Moody, Ralph. *Little Britches*. New York, NY. Bison Books, 1978.

O'Brien, Robert C. *Z for Zachariah*. New York, NY. Simon Pulse, 1987.

St. John, Patricia M. *Star of Light*. Chicago, IL. Moody Press, 1953.

Taylor, Jeannie St. John. *Out at Home*. Grand Rapids, MI. Kregel Publications, 2004.

Taylor, Mildred D. *Roll of Thunder, Hear My Cry*. New York, NY. Puffin Books, 1976.

White, E.B. *Charlotte's Web*. New York, NY. HarperCollins, 2001.

Thank you!

A special thanks goes to these writing workshop students who graciously allowed me to use excerpts of their work in *Reach for the Stars*:

Brandon Beeman

Jacob Beeman

Amy Johnson

Danielle Jurczak

Vera Faye Lobo

Bethany McClenahan

Rachel Mudd

Amber (Lulu) Nix

Amber Schwilling

Ashley Strawser

Maegan Taggart

Alyssa Urailak

You are all writing "stars"!

CPSIA information can be obtained at www.ICGtesting.com
Printed in the USA
BVOW021651250112

281343BV00002B/4/P

9 781931 941198